DESIGN & MAKE IT!

textiles technology

ALEX McARTHUR

CAROLYN ETCHELLS ▪ TRISTRAM SHEPARD

First published in 1997 by
Stanley Thornes (Publishers) Ltd
Ellenborough House
Wellington Street
CHELTENHAM
GL50 1YW

A catalogue record for this book is available from the British Library.

ISBN 0 7487 2471 0

98 99 00 01 02/ 10 9 8 7 6 5 4

Designed and typeset by Carla Turchini
Picture research by Jennie Karrach
Artwork by Anna Braithwaite, Andrew Loft, Hardlines and Tristram Shepard
Printed and bound in Spain by Mateu Cromo

The authors would particularly like to thank the following for their contribution :
Lynn Beech, Anna Braithwaite, Brian Dickie of Skopos, Roy Jarratt, Ruth Rundle and Pauline Treuherz; also Mark Hall, Tracy Leeson and Emma Rough of Minster College, Sheppey, Kent for modelling the project outcomes.

The publishers are grateful to the following for permission to reproduce photographs or other illustrative material:
Andrew Wiard: p. 82 (bottom)
Berghaus: pp. 54, 55
Bridgeman Art Library: pp. 29 (Osterreichische Galerie, Vienna), 32 (Smithsonian Institution, Washington DC)
British Standards Institute: p. 123
British Textiles Technology Group: pp. 65, 66, 92 (top)
Courtaulds Fibres: pp. 94 (bottom), 128
Crafts Council: p. 37 (right)
Cunard: p. 84 (top)
D'oyly Carte / James Hendy design / Alan Wood photography: pp. 20 (middle), 22 (middle and bottom)
Impact Photos: pp. 72 (bottom – Javed A Jafferji), 111 (top and bottom – Ben Edwards) (middle – Nigel Davis)
Intermediate Technology: pp. 36 (Neil Cooper), 52 (top – Simon Ekless) (bottom – Jeremy Hartley)
International Wool Secretariat: p. 56 (left)
Jaeger: p. 115 (bottom)
J.I.C.C: p. 28
John Lewis Photographic Library: p. 72 (top)
Kevin Chapple Gilbert and Sullivan Collection: p. 23 (top left and bottom)
Malden Mills: p. 127
Marks and Spencer: p. 131 (middle)
Martyn Chillmaid: pp. 57 (bottom right), 60 (left), 94 (middle), 95, 110, 123, 138/139 (bottom)
Mary Evans Picture Library: p. 22 (top), 23 (top right), 94 (top)
News International: The Times: p. 121
Niall McInerney: pp. 131 (bottom left), 136 (top)
Nottingham Trent University, Department of Fashion and Textiles, Computer Clothing Research Group: pp. 119 (top left, centre and right) 136(bottom), cover (centre)
Panos Pictures: pp. 37 (left – Jeremy Hartley), 96 (Neil Cooper and Jan Hammond)
Performing Arts Library: p. 20 (bottom)
Pictorial Press: pp. 60 (right), 130 (top – Marcio Madeira) (bottom – Marcio Madeira / Zeppelin)
P & O Cruises: pp. 84 (bottom), 137
Quantas: p. 87
SCOT Innovation: p. 121
Scottish College of Textiles: p. 129 (top – Sarah Taylor)
Scottish Highland Photolibrary: p. 114 (bottom)
Science Photolibrary: pp. 34, cover right (Eye of Science), 92 (bottom – Andrew Syred), 93 (top – Dr Jeremy Burgess) (bottom), 115 (top – Bruce Roberts), 122 (R. Maisonneuve, Publiphoto Diffusion) 125, cover left (Peter Ryan), 129 (bottom left – Claude Nuridsany) (bottom right)
Science Pictures Ltd: pp. 24, 99, 114 (top), 118, 119 (bottom left and right)
Simon Phillips: pp. 47, 68, 74, 107
Still Moving: pp. 56 (right – Ken Paterson), 62 (lower – Doug Corrance)
Susan Kennewell: p. 33 (top right)
Tony Stone Images: p. 117 (top – Ed Pritchard)
Victoria and Albert Museum, by courtesy of the Board of Trustees; photographer R I Davis: pp. 42, 70, 105, 109
Virgin Atlantic Airways Ltd: p. 82 (top)
Walls Birdseye: p117 (bottom)
Wealth of Nations: p. 126
Welbeck Fabrics: p. 120 (bottom)
ZEFA: p. 13, 120 (top – C.Hammell)

Contents

Project Three: A Sea Cruise

Project Suggestions

Introduction

Welcome to Design & Make It: Textiles Technology. *This book has has been written to support you as you work through your GCSE course in Design and Technology. It will help guide you through the important stages of your coursework, and assist your preparation for the final examination paper.*

Long or short?

If you are following a short course, check with your teacher which sections of the book you do not need to cover.

Making it

Whatever your project, remember that the final realisation is particularly important. It is not enough just to hand in your design folder. You must have separate textile products which you have made. The quality of your final realisation must be as high as possible as it counts for a high proportion of the marks.

During your course you will need to develop technical skills in using fabrics and equipment. This is something you can't do just by reading a book! The best way is to watch carefully as different techniques and procedures are demonstrated to you, and practise them as often as possible.

IN YOUR PROJECT

Special 'In Your Project' paragraphs help you to think about how you could apply the content of the pages to your current work.

How to Use this Book

There are two main ways the book might be used.

1   Follow the three design and make projects in sequence over the whole course, including a selection of the suggested activities (i.e. focused practical tasks). This will ensure complete syllabus coverage. You may decide not to take all of them as far as the production of a finished working product.
2   Undertake alternative projects to one or more of those provided and refer to those pages which cover the specific areas of knowledge and understanding defined in the examination syllabus and the KS4 National Curriculum.

Contents

Project guide

The book begins with a coursework guide which summarises the design skills you will need for extended project work. Refer back to these pages throughout the course.

The projects

Three projects are then provided. These each contain a mixture of product analysis and development pages and knowledge and understanding pages (e.g. Embellishment, Fibres and Fabrics) which include short focused tasks. In each of the projects the development of one possible solution has been used as an ongoing example. You could closely base your own work on this solution, but if you want to achieve higher marks you will need to try to come up with ideas of your own.

Project Suggestions

Finally two outline project suggestions are provided. Refer to the Project Guide to help develop your ideas and to ensure you are covering and documenting your coursework in the way the examiners will be looking for.

■ ACTIVITY

Make sure that as part of your design folder you include evidence of having completed a number of short-term focused practical tasks as suggested in the Activity sections.

KEY POINTS

Use the 'Key Points' paragraphs to revise from when preparing for the final examination paper. Three specimen papers are included at the end of the projects.

Beyond GCSE

Textiles and clothing production is one of the fastest growing industries in the world, and UK manufacturers now operate on a global scale.

There are good opportunities for skilled people to work in manufacturing. Another alternative is to train as a textile, fashion, theatre or interior designer, or in design management, marketing and retailing or textile technology. Such people need to be flexible, good communicators, willing to work in teams, and to be computer literate.

There are a wide range of further courses and training opportunities available at various levels which you might like to find out more about.

Choosing and Starting Projects

Identifying suitable design and make projects for yourself is not easy. A carefully chosen project is much more likely to be interesting and easier to complete successfully. Investing time and effort choosing a good project makes progress a lot easier later on.

transport

leisure

food

health

the natural environment

the home

STARTING POINTS

There are a number of different ways you might start a project. Your teacher may have:
► told you exactly what you are required to design
► given you a range of possible design tasks for you to chose from
► left it up to you to suggest a possible project.

If you have been given a specific task to complete you can go straight on to page 8.

If you are about to follow one of the main units in this book, you should go straight to the first page of the task.

If you have been given a number of possible tasks to choose from you should go straight to the section entitled 'Making your Choice'.

However, if you need to begin by making some decisions about which will be the best task for you, then the first stage is to undertake some feasibility studies.

Project Feasibility Studies

Make a start by making a list of:

▷ potential local situations/environments you could visit where you could do some research into the sort of things people there might need (e.g. a local playgroup, a hospital or old people's home, etc.)
▷ people you know outside school who might be able to help by providing information, access and/or advice.

The next stage is to get up and get going. Arrange to visit some of the situations you've listed.

Choose the ones which you would be interested in finding out some more about. Make contact with the people you know, and get them interested in helping you. Tell them about your D&T course, and your project.

For each possible situation you should:

▷ visit the situation or environment
▷ make initial contact with those whose help you will need.

With a bit of luck, after you've done the above you should have a number of ideas for possible projects.

Try to identify what the possible outcomes of your projects might be – not what the final design would be, but the form your final realisation might take, e.g. presentation artwork, a sample, a series of test-pieces, a finished garment or printed fabric made into a product, etc. Think carefully about the following:

▷ Might it be expensive or difficult to make?
▷ Do you have access to the equipment and materials that would be required?
▷ Will you be able to find out how it could be printed or manufactured in quantity?
▷ Does the success of the project depend on important information you might not be able to get in the time available?

Remember that it's important that what you design is suitable for production, even if only in small numbers. It can't be just a one-off item for you or a friend.

security

education

the high street

Don't forget to record all your thoughts and ideas about these initial stages of choosing and starting your project.

Making your Choice

For each of your possible projects work through pages 8 and 9 (Project Investigation) and try planning out a programme of research.

Look back over your starting questions and sources of information:

▷ Could you only think up one or two areas for further research?
▷ Did you find it difficult identifying a range of sources of information?

If this has been the case, then maybe it is not going to prove to be a very worthwhile project.

Ideally, what you're looking for is a project which:

▷ is for a nearby situation you can easily use for research and testing
▷ you can get some good expert advice about.

The project should provide good opportunities for you to do a range of research activities and an expected outcome which:

▷ will make it possible for you to make and test a prototype
▷ will not be too difficult to finally realise.
▷ will be suitable for manufacture.

Finally, one of the most important things is that you feel interested and enthusiastic about the project!

A very important consideration is the testing of a prototype of some sort, and of your final design. How would you be able to do this?

In your project folio provide a full record of the ideas you reject, and the reasons why. This helps provide important evidence of your decision-making skills, and of the originality of your project.

Make sure you discuss your project ideas with a teacher.

If you come up with more than one good idea, find out how many projects you have to submit at the end of your course. You might be able to do one or more of your other ideas at a later date.

Design Folder

✔ My project is to design a...
✔ I am particularly interested in...
✔ I have made a very good contact with...
✔ My prototype can be tested by...
✔ My final outcome will include...

Project Investigation

You will need to find out as much as you can about the people and the situation you are designing for. To do this you will need to identify a number of different sources of information to use for your research.

> Write down what you need to find out more about, and how you could obtain the information.

Starting Questions

Make a list of questions you will have to find answers to.

You should find the following prompts useful:

Why...?	When...?
Where...?	What...?
How many...?	How often...?
How much...?	

> - How often will they want to wear this outfit?
> - How much can they afford to pay?
> - What fabric toys would appeal to a young child?
> - Where will the wall hanging be placed?
> - What items will need to be carried in the bag?

> Make sure your research work is clearly and attractively presented.

Sources of Information

Next, carefully consider and write down potential sources of information you might be able to use to discover the answers to your starting questions.

Work through the research methods on the opposite page. Be sure to give specific answers as far as possible (i.e. name names!).

Across your research, aim to obtain overall a mixture of:

▷ factual information: e.g. size, shape, weight, cost, speed etc.,

▷ information which will be a matter of opinion: i.e., what people think and feel about things, their likes and dislikes, what they find important, pleasing, frustrating, etc.

> Identify a number of sources of information, and undertake the research, remembering to record what you discover.

> The more you plan your research, the more different methods of research you use (e.g. observation, surveys, book-based, site-study etc.), and the more detail you discover, the more marks you will get.

Design Folder

✔ The key things I need to find out about are...
✔ The research methods I am going to use are...
✔ I will be talking to the following people about my project...
✔ I will need to have it all completed by...

Research Methods

Of all the research methods, user-research tends to be the most effective and useful, so you are highly recommended to include some in your investigation. Some form of personal contact is essential to a really successful project.

User-research
Which people could you observe and consult who are directly involved in the situation? To what extent do you consider that you will be able to find out about:

▶ the things they do
▶ the way in which they do them.

As well as asking individuals, you could also undertake a small survey or questionnaire.

Users trips
How can you record your own impressions of the situation? Are there any relevant activities you could try out for yourself to gain first-hand experience? Do you have any recollections of any previous similar experiences you have had?

Site study
In what ways could you document the environment in which the situation is? Which of the following will be relevant?

▶ Historical and geographical factors.
▶ Sociological, economic, political information.
▶ Location.
▶ Layout, facilities .
▶ Sizes and spaces.
▶ Atmosphere – light, colour, texture.
▶ The surrounding environment.

Similar situations
Do you know of any other comparable circumstances in which people are in similar situations, and which might help provide insight and ideas?

Expert opinion
Are there any people you know of who could give you expert professional advice on any aspects of the situation? If you don't know immediately of anyone, how might you set about finding somebody?

Literature search
Has any information about the situation, or a similar situation, been documented already in books, magazines, TV programmes etc.
If you don't already know that such information exists, where could you go to look for it? Don't forget to consider the possibility of using information stored on a computer data-base.

It is also highly advisable to conduct some form of questionnaire. If you have not done one to submit as part of your coursework, make sure that you will have the opportunity to do so this time.

It isn't necessary to use all the research methods in any one project, but you must show you have tried a selection of them.

In Conclusion

When most of your investigation work has been completed you will need to draw a series of conclusions from what you have discovered. What have you learnt about the following things:

▷ What sort of people are likely to be using the product?
▷ Where and when will they be using it?
▷ What particular features will it need to have?
▷ How many should be made?

Design Folder

✔ From my research I found out...
✔ I have discovered that...
✔ The results of my tests show that...

Design Specification

A design specification is a series of statements which describe the possibilities and restrictions of the product. The specification usually includes details about the appearance, size and weight of the product, the features and performance which are expected, and the number to be made.

Writing a Specification

The design specification is a very important document. It describes the things about the design which are fixed and also defines the things which you are free to change. At the end of the project what you have designed will need to be tested and evaluated in relation to the specification to see how closely you have been able to follow it.

Your research conclusions should form the starting point for your specification. For example, if in your conclusions you wrote:

'From the measurements I made of a number of people's backs, I discovered that the best size for the length of my design would be between 30 and 50 cm.'

In the specification you would simply write:

'The garment should be between 30 cm and 50 cm in length.'

The contents of the specification will vary according to the particular product you are designing, but on the next page is a checklist of aspects to consider. Don't be surprised if the specification is quite lengthy. It could easily contain 20 or more statements.

Fixing it

Some statements in the specification will be very specific, e.g.: *'It must be red.'*

Other statements may be very open-ended, e.g.: *'It can be any colour.'*

Most will come somewhere in between, e.g.: *'It should be a bright, primary colour.'*

In this way the statements make it clear what is fixed, and where the designer needs to take the decisions.

Make sure you include as much numerical data as possible in your specification. Try to provide data for anything which can be measured, such as size, weight, quantity, time and temperature.

After you've written the specification, new information may come to light. If it will improve the final product, you can always change any of the statements.

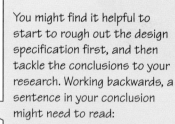

You might find it helpful to start to rough out the design specification first, and then tackle the conclusions to your research. Working backwards, a sentence in your conclusion might need to read:

'From my survey, I discovered that young children are particularly attracted by bright primary colours...'

Specification Checklist

The following checklist is for general guidance. Not all topics will apply to your project.

Use and performance
Write down the main purpose of the product – what it is intended to do. Also define any other particular requirements, such as speed of operation, special features, accessories, etc. Ergonomic information is important here.

Size and weight
The minimum and maximum size and weight will be influenced by things like the components needed and the situation the product will be used and kept in.

Generally the smaller and lighter something is the less material it will use, reducing the production costs. Smaller items can be more difficult to make, however, increasing the production costs.

Appearance
What shapes, colours and textures will be most suitable for the type of person who is likely to use the product? Remember that different people like different things.

These decisions will have an important influence on the materials and manufacturing processes, and are also crucial to ensure final sales.

Safety
A product needs to conform to all the relevant safety standards.
▶ Which of them will apply to your design?
▶ How might the product be misused in a potentially dangerous way?
▶ What warning instructions and labels need to be provided?

Conforming to the regulations can increase production costs significantly, but is an area that cannot be compromised.

Manufacturing cost
This is concerned with establishing the maximum total manufacturing cost which will allow the product to be sold at a price the consumer or client is likely to pay. The specification needs to include details of:
▶ the total number of units likely to be made
▶ the rate of production and, if appropriate
▶ the size of batches.

Maintenance
Products which are virtually maintenance free are more expensive to produce.
▶ How frequently will the product need to be cleaned/laundered?
▶ How easy does this need to be?

Life expectancy
The durability of the product has a great influence on the quantity of materials and components and manufacturing process which will need to be used.

How long should the product remain in working order, providing it is used with reasonable care?

Environmental requirements
In your specification you will need to take into account how your product can be made in the most environmentally friendly way. You might decide to:
▶ specify maximum amounts of some materials
▶ avoid a particular material because it can't be easily re-cycled
▶ state the use of a specific manufacturing process because it consumes less energy.

Other areas
Other statements you might need to make might cover special requirements such as transportation and packaging.

Design Folder

✔ My design will need to...
✔ The main requirements of the people who will use it are...
✔ It will also need to do the following...
✔ It will be no larger than...
✔ It will be no smaller than...
✔ Its maximum weight can be...
✔ It should not be lighter than...
✔ The shapes, colours and textures should...

✔ The design will need to conform to the following safety requirements...
✔ The number to be made or the length of fabric to be printed or woven is...
✔ The following parts of the product should be easily replaceable...
✔ To reduce wastage and pollution it will be necessary to ensure that...

Generating and Developing Ideas

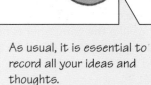

When you start designing you need lots of ideas – as many as possible, however crazy they might seem. Then you need to start to narrow things down a bit by working in more detail and evaluating what you are doing.

Work towards making at least one prototype to test out some specific features of your design. Record the results and continue to refine your ideas as much as you can. Sorting out the final details often requires lots of ideas too.

As you work through this section it is important to remember the following sequence when considering potential solutions:
► record a number of different possibilities
► consider and evaluate each idea
► select one approach as the best course of action, stating why.

First Thoughts

Start by exploring possibilities at a very general level. Spend time doing some of the following:

▷ brainstorming, using key words and phrases or questions which relate to the problem
▷ completing spider-diagrams which map out a series of ideas
▷ using random word- or object-association to spark off new directions
▷ thinking up some good analogies to the situation (i.e. what is it like?)
▷ working from an existing solution by changing some of the elements
▷ experimenting with some ingredients.

Continue doing this until you have at least two or three possible approaches to consider. Make sure they are all completely different, and not just a variation on one idea.

Go back to your design specification. Which of your approaches are closest to the statements you made? Make a decision about which idea to take further, and write down the reasons for your choice.

As usual, it is essential to record all your ideas and thoughts.

Much of your work, particularly early on, will be in the form of annotated sketches.

There are lots of different drawing or illustration techniques which you can use to help you explore and develop your ideas.

Try to use as rich a mixture of them as possible. At this stage they should really be 'rough', rather than 'formal' (i.e. drawn with a ruler). Colour is most useful for highlighting interesting ideas and indicating different materials and textures.

Drawings on their own do not reveal very well what you had in mind, and whether you thought it was a good idea or not.

Words on their own suggest that you are not thinking visually enough.

Aim to use both sketches and words.

Second Thoughts

Working on paper, begin to develop your ideas in more detail. Remember to use a range of three-dimensional drawing techniques as well as words and numbers to help you model your ideas.

Wherever possible consider using a CAD program. Don't forget to print out the various stages you work through, or at least make sure you keep your own copy on disc of the screens you generate.

At some stage you will need to move off the drawing board and try some things out in three dimensions using real materials.

Planning and Making Prototypes

At some stage you will be in a position to bring your ideas into sharper focus by making some form of mock-up or **prototype**. Think carefully about exactly what aspect of your idea you want to test out and about the sort of model which will be most appropriate.

Whatever the form of your final outcome, the mock-up might need to be:

▷ two-dimensional
▷ three-dimensional
▷ at a different scale
▷ made using different materials.

Try to devise some objective tests to carry out on your prototype involving measuring something. Don't rely just on people's opinions.

As you develop your ideas, make sure you are considering the following:

▶ Design – aesthetics, ergonomics, marketing potential, etc.
▶ User requirements – functions and features.
▶ Technical viability – if it could be made.
▶ Manufacturing potential – how it could be made in quantity.
▶ Environmental concerns – if it can be reused, recycled etc.?

Write up the circumstances in which the tests were undertaken, and record your results. Write down some clear statements about:

▷ what you wanted the mock-up to test
▷ the experimental conditions
▷ what you discovered
▷ what decisions you took about your design as a result.

Following your first prototype you may decide to modify it in some way and test it again, or maybe make a second, improved version from scratch. Make sure you keep all the prototypes you make, and ideally take photographs of them being tested.

Sometimes you will need to go back to review the decisions you made earlier, and on other occasions you may need to jump ahead for a while to explore new directions or to focus on a particular detail. Make sure you have worked at both a general and a detailed level.

Design Folder

✔ I chose this idea because...
✔ I developed this aspect of my design by considering...
✔ To evaluate my ideas I decided to make a mock-up which...
✔ The way I tested my mock-up was to...
✔ What I discovered was...
✔ As a result I decided to change...

Planning the Making and the Manufacturing

The final realisation is very important. It presents your proposed design solution rather than the process you used to develop it. Careful planning is essential.

You will also need to be able to explain how your product could be reproduced or manufactured in quantity.

How many?

What you have designed should be suitable for **manufacture**. You should discuss with your teacher how many items or what length of fabric you should attempt to make. This is likely to depend on the complexity of your design and the materials and facilities available in your workshops. It may be that you only make one item, but also provide a clear account of how a quantity of them could be manufactured.

KEEPING A RECORD

Write up a diary record of the progress you made while making. Try to include references to:
▶ things you did to ensure safety
▶ the appropriate use of materials
▶ minimising waste
▶ choosing tools
▶ practising making first
▶ checking that what you are making is accurate enough to work
▶ asking experts (including teachers) for advice
▶ explaining why you had to change your original plan for making.

Paperwork

Before you start planning you will need to ensure that you have a final artwork rough of your design. You will also need a diagram of a pattern for your design (see pages 40–41). This must include all pattern markings, measurements and materials to be used. Ideally there should also be written and drawn instructions which would enable someone else to be able to make up the design from your plans.

Next work out a production flow-chart as follows.

1 List the order in which you will prepare the final artwork or make the main parts of the product. Include as much detail as you can.

2 Divide the list up into a number of main stages, e.g. gathering materials and components, preparing (i.e. marking out/cutting), assembling, finishing.

3 Identify series of operations which might be done in parallel.

4 Indicate the time scale involved on an hourly, daily and weekly basis.

Think carefully about what equipment is available in your school which could save you a considerable amount of time.

You may find you have to change your plans as you go. There is nothing wrong with doing this, but you should explain why you have had to adjust your schedule, and show that you have considered the likely effect on the later stages of production.

What needs to be done by:

● next month
● next week
● next lesson
● the end of this lesson?

Remember to use a wide range of graphic techniques to help plan and explain your making.

Quality Counts

As your making proceeds you will need to check frequently that your work is of acceptable quality.

How accurately will you need to work? What tolerances will be acceptable? How can you judge the quality of the finish?

If you are making a number of identical items you should try to work out ways of checking the quality through a sampling process.

Making

While you are in the process of **making** you must ensure that the tools and materials you are using are the correct ones. Pay particular attention to safety instructions and guidelines.

Try to ensure that you have a finished item at the end, even if it involves simplifying what you do.

Aim to produce something which is made and finished as accurately as possible. If necessary you may need to develop and practise certain skills beforehand.

Planning for Manufacture

You should try to explain how your product would be manufactured in quantity. Work through the following stages of planning for production:

Don't forget that there is also a high proportion of marks for demonstrating skill and accuracy, overcoming difficulties and working safely during the making.

Manufacturing matters

Try asking the following questions about the way your design might be made in quantity:
► What operation is being carried out, and why? What alternatives might there be?
► Where is the operation done and why? Where else might it be carried out?
► When is it done and why? When else might it be undertaken?
► Who carries it out, and why? Who else might do it?
► How is it undertaken, and why? How else might it be done?

Remember that manufacturing is not just about making things. It is also about making them better by making them:
► simpler
► quicker
► cheaper
► more efficient
► less damaging to the environment.

1 Decide which type of production will be most suitable (e.g. batch, mass), depending on the number or amount to be made.
2 Break up the production process into its main parts and identify any sub-assemblies.
3 Consider where jigs and templates could be used. Could CAM be used?

4 List the total number of components and total volume of raw material needed for the production run.
5 Identify what will be made by the main manufacturing company and what will probably need to be bought in ready-made from outside suppliers.
6 Draw up a production schedule. This should show how materials and components will be organised to be available exactly where and when needed. Suggest how the workforce and workspace should be arranged.

7 Decide how quality control systems will be applied to produce the degree of accuracy required.
8 Identify the health and safety issues and plan how to minimise risks.
9 Estimate the manufacturing cost of the product.
10 Review the design of the product and the manufacturing process to see how costs can be reduced.

Design Folder

- ✔ I planned the following sequence of making...
- ✔ I had to change my plan to account for...
- ✔ I used the following equipment and processes...
- ✔ I paid particular attention to safety by...
- ✔ I managed to complete my product by...
- ✔ I worked to the following tolerances...

Testing and Evaluation

You will need to find out how successful your final design solution is. How well does it match the product specification? How well have you worked? What would you do differently if you had another chance?

Testing the Final Solution

To find out how successful your design is you will need to test it out. Some of the ways in which you might do this are by:

▷ trying it out yourself
▷ asking other people to use it
▷ asking experts what they think about it.

As well as recording people's thoughts, observations and opinions, try to obtain some data: how many times it was used, over what periods of time, within what performance limits, etc? This will help you to provide the evidence to show that you have tested your final design out in some way.

To help you decide what to test, you should look back to the statements in your design specification, and focus on the most important ones. If for example the specification stated that a three-year old child must be able to wear it, try to find out how many can. If it must be a colour which would appeal to young children, devise a way of finding out what age-ranges it does appeal to. Make sure you use your target consumer group when carrying out the tests.

Try to ensure that your findings relate directly to the statements in your original specification.

Include as much information and detail as you can.

TEST CHART
• Does the container hold the objects it was designed for ?
• Did you find it easy to fasten and unfasten ?
• Did you find any difficulties gripping the handles ?

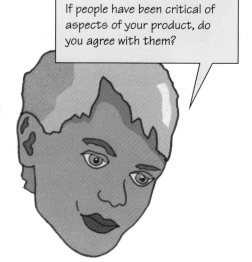

If people have been critical of aspects of your product, do you agree with them?

Don't be too surprised or worried if your product isn't perfect — the important thing is that you can identify what is wrong with it. Can you make some simple suggestions about how it might be improved?

If you had more time:
► what aspects of the product would you try to improve? Refer to your evaluation if you can.
► how would you improve the way you had researched, developed, planned and evaluated your working process?

Final Evaluation

There are two things you need to discuss in the final **evaluation**: the quality of the product you have designed and made, and the process you went through while designing and making it.

How successful is your final product? Comment on things like:

▷ how it compares with your original intentions
▷ how well it solves the original problem
▷ the materials you used
▷ what it looks like
▷ how well it works
▷ what a potential consumer said
▷ what experts said
▷ whether it could be made cheaply enough in quantity
▷ the ways in which it could be improved.

Justify your evaluation by including references to what happened when you tested it.

Don't forget to write about both the product and the process.

Try to identify a mixture of good and bad points about your proposal and method of working.

You will gain credit for being able to demonstrate that you are aware of weaknesses in what you have designed and the way that you have designed and made it.

How well have you worked? Imagine you suddenly had more time, or were able to start again, and consider:

▷ Which aspects of your investigation, design development work and making would you try to improve, or approach in a different way?
▷ What did you leave to the last minute, or spend too much time on?
▷ Which parts are you most pleased with, and why?
▷ How well did you make the final realisation?

Design Folder

✔ The people I showed my ideas (drawings and final product) to said...
✔ I was able to try my product out by...
✔ I discovered that...

✔ I could improve it by...
✔ I didn't do enough research into...
✔ I spent too long on...
✔ I should have spent more time on...
✔ The best aspect is...
✔ I have learnt a lot about...

Project Presentation

The way you present your project work is extremely important. Remember you won't be there to explain it all when it's being assessed! You need to make it as easy as possible for an examiner to see and understand what you have done.

Telling the Story

All your investigation and development work needs to be handed in at the end, as well as what you have made. Your design folder needs to tell the story of the project. Each section should lead on from the next, and clearly show what happened next, and explain why. Section titles and individual page titles can help considerably.

There is no single way in which you must present your work, but the following suggestions are all highly recommended:

▷ Bind all the pages together in some way. A ring or end-binder is probably best. If you use an end binder make sure you also staple the sheets together in case the binder falls off.
▷ Add a cover with a title and an appropriate illustration
▷ Make it clear which the main sections of development are
▷ Add in titles or running headings to each sheet to indicate what aspect of the design you were considering at that particular point in the project.

Presentation is something you need to be thinking about throughout your project work. Try to ensure you have at least one A3 sheet which covers each of these headings.

Some stages may need several sheets!

Binding methods

Presenting your Design Folder Sheets

▷ Always work on standard size paper, either A3 or A4.

▷ Aim to have a mixture of written text and visual illustration on each sheet.

▷ You might like to design a special border to use on each sheet.

▷ Include as many different types of graphs, tables, charts and diagrams as possible, especially those done on computer.

▷ When including photographs, don't stick them on with sticky tape, staples or photo-corner mounts. A small amount of paper adhesive applied evenly all the way round the edge is the best way of fixing them on.

▷ Think carefully about the lettering for titles, and don't just put them anywhere and anyhow. Try to choose a height and width of lettering which will be well balanced on the whole page. If the title is too big or boldly coloured it may dominate the sheet. If it is thin or light it might not be noticed.

Presenting your Project Report

This is a more formal document and might for example:

▷ describe and discuss the development and modification process
▷ document detailed research material and analysis of information.

It should also include a detailed project evaluation.

If at all possible, type up the report. This could be done on a word processor or, ideally, using a DTP program. Remember to think carefully about the design of the layout of text, and to include illustrations such as photographs and statistical graphs and charts as appropriate.

Your project report could include:
► a cover
► an introduction
► your investigation and development
► test results
► your final evaluation
► an appendix.

Project One: Introduction

ON STAGE

Designing for the Theatre (page 24)

Putting it Together (page 44)

Cutting it out (page 42)

A local theatre director intends to stage a production of Gilbert and Sullivan's The Mikado next season. He is looking for someone to design and make some costumes and some fabrics for the stage set.

Read the following letter carefully:

With reference to our recent meeting I am pleased to confirm that we would like to commission you to produce the costumes and fabrics for our forthcoming production of *The Mikado*.

We intend to have a very simple stage set, and to use the shapes, colours and patterns of the costumes, screens, banners and other fabric items to bring the opera alive.

We will need to receive from you:
- initial ideas for the costumes
- test pieces
- a sample costume for one of the main characters and/or
- a sample fabric for the stage set.

Enclosed is a brief outline of the story and descriptions of the main characters and one of the scenes which will be required.

I look forward to seeing your ideas and discussing their potential at our first production meeting.

Yours sincerely

John Davies

Theatre Director

Clarifying the Brief

▷ Make a list of all the things the theatre director expects you to do.

▷ Read the **story outline** and descriptions of the **characters** and **scenes**, which you will find on page 22–3.

Creating an effect with Colour (page 28)

Embellishing Fabrics (page 32)

ON STAGE

Colouring Fabric (page 36)

Adapting a Pattern (page 40)

Visual Research

You will need to start looking out for examples of Japanese costumes and sketch examples of **accessories**, **surface patterns** and **motifs**.

First Thoughts

Brainstorm your initial thoughts and ideas using labelled sketches and/or spider diagrams.

▷ What might the costumes be like?
▷ How could textiles be used effectively as part of the stage set?

Traditional Japanese screens could be arranged on stage. Easy to move around during Opera

More modern 2 dimensional geometric screen, With painted fabric.

Mix of plain and patterned fabric. Fabric draped to make a landscape.

Modern T-shirt can be painted with Japanese patterns or tie-dyed in bold colours. Can be worn with trousers and fabric belt.

Set in 1920's

painted motif

Traditional layered and tied Kimonos for main characters.

21

The Mikado

ON STAGE

Understanding the atmosphere, setting and main characters of the storyline is vital to the successful design of costumes and stage-sets.

You will need to make notes on the following:

▷ Where is the musical set?
▷ What **period** is it set in?
▷ What is the **mood** of the story?
▷ What are the **personalities** of the main characters?

If you prefer you could choose to design your costumes for a different play or musical. You will need to obtain similar information about the **characters** and **settings**.

About *The Mikado*

The Mikado has always been the most popular of all Gilbert and Sullivan's works. It was first performed on the 14th March 1885 in London. During the 1880s, when it was written, Britain was swept by a craze for everything Japanese, and the comic opera provided the opportunity for some splendid costumes and exotic scenery.

Although set in a mythical Japanese village, *The Mikado* is in fact a satire on 19th century Britain. For example, *The Mikado*'s ideas of appropriate punishments include forcing railway vandals to travel on exceedingly slow trains!

Revival of the Mikado at the Savoy Theatre, 1896

Enter procession of YUM-YUM's school fellows, heralding YUM-YUM, PEEP-BO, and PITTI-SING

THE THREE	Three little maids from school are we, Pert as a schoolgirl well can be, Filled to the brim with girlish glee, Three little maids from school.
YUM-YUM	Everything is a source of fun
PEEP-BO	Nobody's safe, for we care for none!
PITTI-SING	Life is a joke that's just begun
THE THREE	Three little maids from school!
All (dancing)	Three little maids who, all awary, Come from a ladies' seminary, Freed from its genius tutelary –
THE THREE (suddenly demure).	Three little maids from school!

The Characters and the Plot

The storyline and characters are wildly improbable.

▷ The Mikado is the very grand Emperor of Japan.
▷ Nanki-Poo is the Mikado's son. He disguises himself as a wandering minstrel in order to escape the attentions of Katisha.
▷ Katisha, a brazen, grotesque and blood-thirsty elderly lady, is determined to marry Nanki-Poo.
▷ Yum-Yum is the schoolgirl who Nanki-Poo falls in love with, but she is already engaged to Ko-Ko.
▷ Ko-Ko is the flirtatious Lord High Executioner.

The other main characters include Pooh-Bah (the Lord High Everything Else) and Pish-Tush (an officious nobleman), and a chorus of School Girls, Nobles, Guards and Coolies.

After a series of misunderstandings Nanki-Poo eventually gets to marry Yum-Yum, and Ko-Ko avoids marrying Katisha.

The scenes

Act 1 is set in the courtyard of Ko-Ko's palace in Titipu. Act II is in Ko-Ko's garden

The setting – Japanese style

In the second half of the 19th Century the Japanese were adapting to Western practices, altering their social and legal rules, their clothing, and the whole outlook of their country.

Hairstyles were the easiest and cheapest to alter. In 1873 the Emperor set a trend by having his 'top-knot' cut off. It was increasingly common at this time to see Japanese people dressed in a combination of Western dress and a traditional kimono.

For centuries Japanese women had sewn their own and their family's clothes. In contrast to the simple design of the kimono, Western dress was complicated and required a totally different way of sewing. At first only the very rich could afford to alter their style of dress.

■ ACTIVITY

Find out more about the ways in which Western and Japanese cultures were influenced by each other during the second half of the 19th Century. What part did the new printing, production and transport technologies of the time play?

Designing for the Theatre (1)

ON STAGE

Designing theatrical costumes is not the same as designing garments for everyday life. Different fabrics and methods of production are needed.

Costume Design

One of the most important features of **costume design** is that the garments look distinctive from a distance. They may have to contrast or harmonise with other costumes, or with the scenery. To achieve this you may need to use fabrics, colours and decorations that would not normally be used for everyday wear.

Costumes may need to reflect a particular culture or period of history. At the same time they might be for a character who lives in great wealth or extreme poverty, in which case the garments could be very elaborate, or threadbare.

Sometimes costumes need to help emphasise the nature of the character being played. For example, visual references to a lion could help represent someone who can become angry and ferocious, yet is also majestic.

*19th Century
Victorian dress*

Victorian woman

*Georgian dress
1700–1790*

Production Methods

For the main characters only one copy of a costume design will be required. This type of **production** is described as '**one-off**'. It might be made by one person, or a small group of people.

Some productions have large crowd scenes, or a chorus where the costumes required are the same or very similar. In this case a '**batch**' system of production would be used. This would involve several people working together, sharing the tasks and the equipment to make a number of very similar garments. Patterns would be carefully worked out to ensure minimum wastage and some parts would be cut together to save time.

Costumes have to be easy to put on (particularly if a 'quick change' is needed between scenes) and easy to maintain as they are likely to get dirty or torn quite quickly. It is also essential that they are comfortable to wear and easy to move around in.

Setting the Scene

Settings can be made from many materials. Metals, plastics, wood and fabrics are all used to create **stage sets**. Things are not always what they seem, however. Many surfaces are painted on to a flat wood or canvas, and textures and shadows added to give the effect of different materials.

Sometimes there is very little actual 'scenery'. The clever use of props, costumes and lighting on their own can be enough to create the mood and atmosphere of the setting.

Single sets are the easiest to design. Changes of scenery present a more demanding challenge.

The role of the set designer is to:

▷ represent the play's atmosphere
▷ allow enough space for the actors to move or dance
▷ to ensure that the performers are always visible
▷ create scenery which can be changed quickly and easily
▷ work within the budget.

The effectiveness and originality of the solutions to these problems are a measure of the success and skill of the designer.

Designing with Fabrics

Flowing fabric

Explore the use of fabrics as loose banners, streamers, hand-held flags or long ribbons (like those used by gymnasts). You might create fans of different shapes out of the fabric, and paint motifs on them to represent the place of the action or to reinforce the character.

Think about long strips of fabric hung from the ceiling, or 'flown-in', i.e. tied to long battens or poles which can be raised or lowered on ropes. These strips can be painted with scenes or motifs. They could be front or back lit. If lit from the front they can create areas of strong colour or help provide a focal point for a scene. When lit from the back some materials will become transparent, allowing the audience to see silhouettes.

Free-standing fabric

Experiment with the possibilities of using **free-standing flats**. These are made from fabric stretched over a wooden frame. They are then stiffened with glue and resin to form a hard surface for painting. The most common size for a base flat is 4 metres high by 2 metres wide. You could create scale models of scenes in one quarter size.

Alternatively, other free-standing shapes such as squares, pyramids and triangles can be covered with a variety of fabrics to give them a surface texture or design. The advantage of this is that the shapes can be used again easily .

Fabric fields

Fabric can be used effectively to represent the sea, a river, a field or a garden by placing it loosely on the floor. The actors could, for example, then use it to play out a scene where there is a shipwreck, gradually lifting it so that it covers their heads so that it appears as if they are drowning.

I had been commissioned to design the sets and costumes for the 'Diary of a Noblewoman', a play which only has one character, a Japanese noblewoman who appears at six different stages of her life.

I used muslin for the costume and muslin drapes for the set. The character added a new piece of material to her kimono for each new scene. Each layer was a shade of jade blue which got deeper as the character aged, but left a lower border of the lighter colour.

The muslin drapes gave colour washes of blues and magenta. These were sometimes backlit to show a formal Japanese garden in silhouette.

KEY POINTS

● There are some important differences between designing theatrical costumes and garments to be worn for everyday life.
● One-off or batch production is used to make costumes for the theatre.

Designing for the Theatre (2)

You will find it helpful to study some existing costumes and compare them with ordinary clothes.

Dressing Mr Jolly

'I work as a designer for television programmes and commercials. Recently I was asked to create the costumes for the characters and puppets for a children's programme.

The main character was called 'Mr Jolly'. During the programme he acts the part of other characters from nursery rhymes and stories. For one episode he needed a costume for 'The Old Woman Who Lived in a Shoe'.

The programme director felt it was important that the children still recognised Mr Jolly, even when he was dressed like a woman!

In my design I needed to take the following into consideration:

▶ the character
▶ what action the script required the character to do
▶ what fabrics, colours and styles would work well with Mr Jolly's original costume.

▶ the general visual style of the programme
▶ how quickly the costume had to be put on and taken off
▶ the age of the viewers
▶ the available budget
▶ when it needed to be ready by.

The idea I came up with was to use Mr Jolly's original yellow shirt and purple trousers and add a pinafore, cap, wig and glasses.

The costume needed to look 'larger than life' and like a pantomime dame. I used exaggerated colours and patterns and included an outsize pocket for Mr Jolly to hide his props in, as required by the script. Simple accessories were used to keep the time for changing to a minimum, and to keep the whole costume easy and cheap to make.'

Garment Disassembly and Evaluation

You will need to make a comparison between the way in which **stage costumes** and **everyday garments** are designed, constructed and finished. Examining existing products in detail and taking them apart to discover how they have been assembled is a good way to do this.

See if you can obtain a stage costume – if not base your study on the one shown on the right. You will also need a discarded garment such as a pair of trousers, a jacket or a shirt. Ideally it should have some form of decoration or interesting fastenings on it.

Make sketches of the back, front and inside of the garments. You may find it helpful to turn them inside out.

Examine the garments carefully and draw a diagram of all the pattern pieces which would have been needed to make them.

Wide sleeves and loose cut are comfortable but the length and shape are not practical.

Bright, varied fabrics are eyecatching and help to establish the character/theme.

A heavy layered garment looks effective on stage but is not suitable for everyday wear.

Elaborate, decorative fastening. This has a strong impact on stage but takes too long to tie for a practical garment.

How would you describe the everyday garment?

▷ What sort of person might wear it and on what sort of occasions?
▷ What moods and feeling do any colours, textures or patterns suggest?
▷ Where are the seams?
▷ What fabrics have been used, and how might they have been printed or dyed?

▷ Are there any materials which cannot be seen from the outside?
▷ What trimmings and fastenings have been used?
▷ Where are the brand and manufacturer's labels and what information do they provide?
▷ Is the garment in good condition?

Do you think it is a successful piece of design?

▷ What are the good points and bad points about the design?
▷ Can you suggest any improvements?
▷ How well has it survived wear and tear, and being cleaned?
▷ Is it still 'in fashion'?

Apply the questions above to the stage costume.

▷ Which ones are not relevant?
▷ Which produce contrasting answers to those for the everyday garment?

Write a conclusion which summarises the similarities and differences in the designs of stage costumes and everyday garments.

IN YOUR PROJECT

▶ Describe and evaluate a traditional Japanese costume. Sketch textile prints, patterns, colours and the shape of garments. Make small sketches of the pattern pieces they might have used. Sketch and colour some typical Japanese textile prints.
▶ See if you can think of anyone who might have seen a performance of *The Mikado*. It would be interesting to hear what they thought about its costumes and staging.
▶ Are there any videos of *The Mikado* you can watch?

ON STAGE

design disassembly

Shoulder seam. The cut is smart, comfortable and practical.
Hanging loop. Practical for storage.
Armhole.
Button holes.
Facing.
Lining.
Care label Easy care fabric.
Piping in contrasting colour. Smart details emphasise the simple cut.
Patch pocket with top stitching. Strong and practical.
Buttons. Easy to use, a strong and practical fastening.

Creating an Effect with Colour

Colour can be used to create all sorts of dramatic effects. It can alter the way we feel by creating different moods. Colours can be in harmony or contrast with each other.

Japanese Noh theatre costume

Colour Associations

Traditionally the colour of clothing has been considered highly significant. It is often used to create distinction between the sexes and classes. For example, the ancient Persians restricted the number of colours women were allowed to wear. Today we still associate blue with a baby boy and pink with a baby girl.

In Western cultures these distinctions have largely disappeared, but in some societies, such as India for example, colour is still invested with symbolic meaning.

100%   0%

The Colour Wheel

▷ The **primary colours** are red, blue and yellow.
▷ The **secondary colours** are purple, green and orange. These are produced by mixing two primary colours together.
▷ The **tertiary colours** are produced by mixing a primary colour with an adjacent secondary colour.
▷ **Complementary colours** are opposite each other on the colour wheel (e.g. blue and orange). These colours create contrast.
▷ **Harmonious colours** are close to each other on the colour wheel. These colours create harmony.
▷ A single colour (e.g. red) is described as the **hue**.
▷ The hue can be changed by adding white to make it lighter (a **tone**), or black to make it darker (a **shade**).
▷ The reds, yellows and oranges on one side of the colour circle are known as '**warm**' colours, while the blues and greens opposite are called '**cold**' colours.

Eastern Influences

During the nineteenth century a number of international exhibitions were held in Europe. The designs of the Japanese had an enormous impact on Western approaches to colour, composition and design. Many artists collected Japanese woodcuts and artefacts and based their own designs on patterns and unusual colour combinations such as turquoise and coral.

The decorations of Japanese Noh costumes influenced artists such as Gustav Klimt. He had his own collection, and their influence can be seen in his paintings. His figures are often dressed in colourful and decorative robes.

Fulfilment by Gustav Klimt (1862-1918)

ACTIVITY

Look closely at the Noh costume and the work of Gustav Klimt. Use them as the basis for a series of sample patterns using either:

▶ harmonious colours, or
▶ contrasting colours.

IN YOUR PROJECT

Suggest and describe the type of colours needed for the production. Suggest some special effects which could be created by the lighting.

KEY POINTS

- Traditionally colour has always been invested with significance.
- Colours are either primary, secondary or tertiary.
- Colours can be used to create harmony and contrast.
- Colour is always affected by light and texture.
- Fabric texture can influence its effect on stage.

On Stage

Colour

By using different colours and types of light on stage it is possible to vary the colours of the costumes and scenery without actually changing them.

Different types of light alter the colours of the things they illuminate: at different times of the day and year, sunlight can range from a golden brown to harsh yellow or bright blue. There are also different types of artificial light. For example, the colour red will appear to be:

▷ orange under a tungsten light
▷ bluish under a fluorescent tube
▷ brown under a yellow sodium street lamp
▷ black under a green mercury lamp.

At the same time the hue of the actor's skin will alter under different kinds of lighting.

The colours of costumes also need to be considered in relation to the colours of the set.

These are very important considerations when designing for the theatre.

Texture

Fabrics have **texture** as well as colour. Decorative techniques such as collages and three-dimensional effects may 'catch the light' and create a shimmering effect. Gold and other metallic fabrics and threads may enhance this effect. Some fabrics, such as satin weaves, 'shine' more than others because their smooth surface reflects the light.

Techniques for creating unusual textures are presented on pages 32–35.

Writing a Specification/Developing Ideas

ON STAGE

A design brief is the general statement of what the company or client requires. A specification is compiled by the designer after the client's needs have been clarified. It is a list of possibilities and restrictions and it allows the designer to think of the final outcome in more detail.

It was good to meet up with you yesterday and to see your first ideas.

I hope it is now clearer as to exactly what we require, and that you can now go on to develop your ideas in more detail. Just remember that I'm depending on you to come up with something stunning! I'm greatly looking forward to seeing your final proposals at our next meeting.

Until then

Writing a Specification

Begin by looking through all your research and write a short conclusion. This should help you focus on things about your design which are fixed and those you will be able to change. For example there may be strict limitations on using a particular technique if it is too costly or too time-consuming. Consider the areas below.

Function
Which character is your costume going to be for, or which scene is your fabric for? What particular requirements are there?

Aesthetics
You need to think about the overall visual appearance of your design. This is what people will notice first and what they think and feel is important. It includes things such as line, colour, texture, finish, style, shape, form, size, proportion, decoration and patterns. This is not fixed. It will be possible to experiment with many different ideas.

Safety
Considerations should always be given to the user of the finished item and the environment in which it will be used. There is legislation which sets safety standards for textile items which have been developed to protect the consumer. Your costume is slightly different in that it will not go on sale to the general public but safety must still be considered.

Materials
Durability: how hard-wearing does this garment have to be? How often will it be worn?
Maintenance: how often will the garment need to be washed, dried and ironed? Will it be possible to have it dry-cleaned?
Aesthetic properties: will the fabric need to drape well or have texture? At this stage the material to be used is up to you to choose.

Cost
Always an important consideration, it will have a great influence on the materials, trimmings and manufacturing processes used. Materials are usually the most expensive consideration when designing something in school. In industry, labour costs are also very high and the final design will depend a lot on what the client is willing to spend. At this stage you may be able to say, 'It must cost no more than...'

Specification
- My costume is for Katisha
- The colours must be...
- The style and shape must be...
- The material must be...
- Safety aspects include...
- It must cost no more than...
- It must co-ordinate with the rest of the production.

■ ACTIVITY

In your project folder write a specification for your design. State what is fixed and what you are free to experiment with.

Developing Initial Design Ideas

embroidered back panel.

YUM YUM

quilted waistband

Fabric samples

tie dye circles

zip decorating appliqué circle

section of embroidery

Textile techniques

Now you have completed a thorough investigation you will need to become more familiar with a range of textile techniques, such as:

▷ embellishment (see pages 32 to 35) and
▷ colouring fabrics (see pages 36 to 39).

Make sure you do the activities and practise your skills. You will be able to use your knowledge to develop more sophisticated designs.

Exploring possible ideas

At this stage try not to form fixed ideas about what you will eventually make. Use notes and quick sketches to get your ideas down. Do not be too fussy about your drawings. Remember to:

▷ annotate...
▷ suggest...
▷ show...
▷ suggest...

Second thoughts

Look carefully at your ideas and evaluate them. Look again at your specification and remind yourself of any limitations to your final design, such as cost.

▷ Note down your thoughts in your project folder.
▷ Discuss your ideas with your teacher and friends.

stencil and applique design.

KATISHA

Square, angular cut reflects the character.

bead

braid

The bright colours give a good effect on stage. The clashing purple and red show Katisha's unpleasant character

Tie-dye checks

Tie-dye stripes

BACK VIEW

Printed fabric screen stretched over a wooden frame

Painted fabric screen draped with tie dyed fabric to represent water.

hanging flags

Developing a final idea

Develop what you consider to be your most promising idea in more detail. You will need to think about:

▷ adapting a pattern (see pages 40 to 41)
▷ cutting out (see page 42 to 43) and
▷ planning the making of the final product (see pages 46 to 47).

For the final meeting with the director you will also need to prepare a presentation drawing showing colour, detailed annotation and if possible small samples of fabrics you intend to use.

Make sure you give your reasons for choosing your final design idea.

Project presentation

Remember to think about the quality of presentation of the development of your design ideas. Use a variety of techniques such as mood-boards, photographs, sketches, colour-boards, swatches and test pieces.

Embellishing Fabrics (1)

ON STAGE

Embellishing means to decorate. A garment can be made more original and interesting by adding decoration. Practise new techniques such as appliqué by making up small test-pieces or samples. These will help make the texture of your designs more interesting.

Rising Sun Quilt by Mary Totten, New York c. 1830

Appliqué

Appliqué is a very old textile technique. It involves applying one piece of fabric to another in order to decorate it. The oldest existing piece of appliqué work dates from 980 BC. The technique was used throughout Europe in the Middle Ages. Necessity drove pioneers in America to produce patchwork and appliqué quilts. It is practised in cultures all over the world including India, Pakistan, Russia and Central and South America.

■ ACTIVITY

Make some samples.

Produce a simple appliqué motif.

Make a creative applique collage by experimenting with different fabric textures, stitches, threads and colour.

You will need the following: a sewing machine, needles, threads, fabric scissors, a fabric marker or tailor's chalk, scraps of different fabrics and a medium-weight woven fabric, such as calico, for the background.

1 Draw a motif onto the fabric and cut it out. You could use a design that you have already sketched or found.

2 Pin and tack the fabric motif onto the background material. If the fabric is very lightweight or stretches you may have to back stiffen it with Bonda-web or Inter-facing.

3 Set your machine on zig-zag stitch and carefully sew round your motif exactly on the raw edge of the fabric. As well as being decorative, this may also stop the edges from fraying.

Interfacing is used when making garments to strengthen things such as button stands, collars and cuffs. It may be woven, knitted or bonded and comes in many different weights so you can pick one to match your fabric.

Creating samples/test-pieces

Making samples is very useful for a number of reasons.

▷ You can find out what effects can be created by using various techniques.

▷ They enable you to experiment and have fun without worrying too much about making mistakes or things not turning out as expected.

▷ You might discover exciting ideas that you can use later on

▷ They encourage you to practise and develop your skills before making your final garment.

Textile by Susan Kennewell

Make sure you keep all your samples and include them in your design folder.

Think carefully about how to combine your experiments into a collage.

▷ Where will the different pieces be placed?

▷ Which colours and patterns will be placed together?

What overall shape will it be?

■ ACTIVITY

1. Look around your home and go through your wardrobe and look for examples of appliqué.
Illustrate them in your design folder. Describe the materials used and how effective they are.

2. Find out more about appliqué techniques by looking in the library. See if you can discover what reverse appliqué is.

3. Produce a short illustrated account of some aspect of appliqué that interests you – for example work from India or Russia.

▶ What makes it special to that country?
▶ What materials, motifs, shapes and colours are typically used?

IN YOUR PROJECT

▶ Would appliqué be a good technique to use to decorate the garment you are designing?

▶ What ideas have you got for experimenting with sample pieces?

KEY POINTS

● Use models, samples and test pieces when developing your designs.

● Appliqué involves applying one fabric to another in order to create colourful decorative textile effects.

● Interfacing is used to strengthen fabric.

● Different stitches can be used to sew fabrics together, and can add to the decorative effect.

Embellishing Fabrics (2)

There are other ways to decorate fabrics. Some can be used with appliqué either to enhance it or to create a more three-dimensional effect.

Fastenings can be decorative as well as functional.

Velcro: made from woven nylon hooks and loops. (magnified x15)

Padding

Your appliqué work (or part of it) can be padded by inserting a piece of wadding or stuffing behind the fabric pieces. This creates a three-dimensional effect and can give your work added depth.

There are also more intricate and detailed effects which can be achieved by using hand and machine embroidery, sequins and beading.

Remember that very fine details may not been seen on stage unless they are made using threads and trimmings which glisten or create texture. These can be very eye-catching under stage lights.

Quilting

Quilting is a technique which can create texture and definition. It involves placing wadding between two layers of fabric and stitching on top to create a pattern.

Layering

Quilting is also one of the best ways to insulate an anorak or a bedcover. Polyester wadding is designed to trap as much air as possible within the structure of the fabric. Air is trapped between the three layers of fabric. Stitching on the three layers is kept to a minimum as too many thin areas reduces the insulation.

Top Layer
Wadding
Bottom Layer (Lining)

How to quilt

1 Transfer your design onto the top layer of fabric using the direct tracing method, tailor's chalk or a fabric marker pen.

2 Put the three layers of fabric together and tack them . This will prevent the fabric from puckering later on.

3 Now you can stitch around your design. By hand bring the needle through the layers of fabric from the wrong side, making sure it goes straight through and not at an angle. Push the needle straight through them again to make a small, straight stitch. Repeat this stitch to make an evenly spaced line.

It is quicker to use machine stitching. Use a fairly large straight stitch or an open zig-zag stitch.

Remove the tacking when finished.

Blanket stitch. Can be used decoratively or to finish a seam.

Running stitch used to create design motifs.

Chain stitch

Cross stitch

Embroidery

To create **embroidery**, threads of different colours are stitched onto the fabric to form a pattern. This can be done by hand or by machine. Many domestic machines can produce pre-programmed patterns. The machine can also be used for free-style **machine embroidery** by dropping the feed dog, removing the presser foot and moving the fabric about under the needle while stretched in a tambour frame.

Industrial embroidery machines are often used in industry to produce badges, logos and names as well as motifs and patterns.

Fastenings

As well as being functional, **fastenings** can also be used to decorate a garment. Fastenings may need to be:

▷ wind or waterproof
▷ invisible
▷ easy to open and close
▷ strong
▷ washable.

■ ACTIVITY

Divide the following fastenings into those which are purely functional and those which could also be decorative: Velcro, buttons, hooks and eyes, toggles, poppers, ties and bows, press studs, frogging, zips.

Toggles, zips and buttons used decoratively on a costume.

Making your own buttons

It is possible to buy kits which allow you to cover buttons with your own fabric. You could paint or dye the fabric yourself, or maybe embroider it.

Try making a button by using something like an old curtain ring and weaving and sewing across it with various strips of fabric, yarns and threads.

a. wind   b. weave   c. embroider   d. embellish

bead

make thread loop

IN YOUR PROJECT

Which of the techniques described on these pages could best be used to decorate the garment you are designing?

Mount all your samples in your design folder in a visually exciting way. Write a short evaluation for each of the samples. Consider the following:
▶ Has it created the desired effect?
▶ How difficult was it?
▶ Did it take a long time?
▶ What is its creative potential for your project?

KEY POINTS

● Padding and quilting can produce a three-dimensional effect.
● Quilting is a very good way to insulate a garment.
● Very intricate details can be achieved with hand or machine embroidery.
● Some fastenings are decorative as well as functional.

ON STAGE

enhancement of fabrics

Colouring Fabric [1]

ON STAGE

You can colour your own fabric by using one of the many dyeing and printing techniques which have been developed over the centuries.

Tie and dye, batik and silk painting are resist techniques. Printing techniques include block printing, screen printing and transfer printing. Others involve direct application of the colour using fabric paints, fabric pens and fabric crayons.

Tie and Dye

Tie and dye is one of the oldest methods of dyeing cloth and some of the best examples originate from India, Africa and Japan. Areas of the fabric are tied with thread or string so that when the cloth is immersed in dye, the tightness of the string resists the dye and prevents it from penetrating to the tied areas. This is known as **resist dyeing**.

Modern techniques for tie and dye are very similar to traditional ones. As well as folding, sewing and binding small objects into the cloth, bulldog clips, staples, pegs and rubber bands are also useful aids.

Tie and dye techniques

First tie up the fabric. Wet the material in clean water and squeeze. Immerse it in the dye and then rinse it thoroughly before untying. Finally leave it to dry. The material can then be re-tied and dyed in a second colour if required.

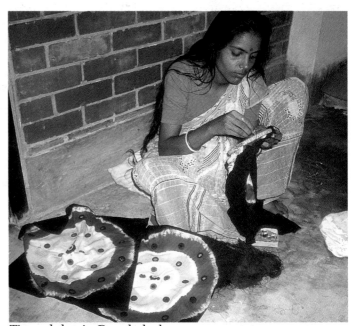

Tie and dye in Bangladesh

Marbled effect
Crumple up fabric into ball and bind.

Stripes/pleats
Pleat fabric in length and tie at intervals with string or rubber bands.

Circles
Lift pieces of fabric and bind. Can vary in size and spaces between circles.

Square tied patterns
Follow the diagrams for dramatic sunburst effects.

ON STAGE

enhancement of fabrics

Batik

Batik uses wax to stop dye penetrating the fabric

Silk Painting

Silk painting uses **gutta** (outliner) as a resist.

Silk Georgette by Judy Dwyer

Materials for Dyeing

The natural fibres – wool, cotton, linen and silk – dye extremely well as they are very absorbent. Man-made fibres can be dyed but cplours are generally not as strong as on natural fibres.

The colour of the fabric you start with is very important. If you dye a white fabric blue, it will turn out blue. If you dye a yellow fabric blue it will turn out green. Look at the information about the colour circle on page 28.

Calico

Calico is a fabric you may find useful throughout your project. It is a plain weave cotton cloth which may be bleached or unbleached. Calico can be bought in different weights. Although it does not drape well it is ideal for dying and printing.

Dyes

Japanese herbalists developed a range of natural dyes. One of the most common was indigo which became the Japanese national colour for workwear.

Until the 1850s all dyes were natural in origin. Then a great deal of research into chemical dyestuffs began and the science became highly developed in France, Germany and England.

The **chemical dyes** were so successful that by the beginning of the twentieth century synthetic dyes were used for most of the coloured textiles produced in Europe and America. They have several advantages over natural dyes:

▶ the colours are much brighter and cleaner
▶ they are much cheaper
▶ they are easier to make

▶ because they are made to scientific formulae the same colour can be reproduced again and exactly matched.

Scientists continue to research dye development. Today textile manufacturers have thousands of different colours to choose from.

■ ACTIVITIES

▶ Find out what dyes you have available in school or are available in the shops, such as hot and cold-water dyes, micron dyes and craft dyes.
▶ Produce your own small samples of tie and dye.
▶ Try tie and dyeing an old T-shirt at home.
▶ Other methods of resist dyeing include batik and silk painting. Investigate one of these techniques.
▶ Find out more about making your own dyes from natural sources.

IN YOUR PROJECT

▶ Would tie and dye be a good technique to use to decorate all or part of the garment you are making?
▶ Take colour and pattern symbolism into account.
▶ What embellishment techniques could you combine with Tie and Dye?

⚠ SAFETY FIRST!

• Wear an apron and use rubber gloves.
• Mix dyes over newspaper.
• Dyes will stain so make sure you do not splash them onto floors, walls, clothing and skin
• Wash up bowls, brushes, etc., immediately after use.

KEY POINTS

● Tie and dye is a resist method for dyeing fabric.
● Natural fibres are the best for dyeing as they are very absorbent.
● It is important to think carefully about the colours you use when dyeing.
● The way in which the fabric is tied will affect the final design.

Colouring Fabric [2]

Stencilling

Stencilling is where shapes are cut from a piece of paper. The stencil is placed on the fabric and paint is applied through the cut-outs with a special brush or sponge.

Stencilling is another decorative art form which the Japanese excelled at. The craft reached its peak between 1603 and 1868 (the Tokugawa Shogunate Dynasty) and created the opportunity for people outside the ruling class to wear brightly coloured patterned clothing.

The designs became very complex. Wooden stencils were replaced by layers of paper and they were cut using a wide variety of blades and awls. Sometimes parts of the stencil were held together by a very fine silk thread.

Floral and plant motifs such as irises, cherry blossom, chrysanthemum, maple leaf, bamboo, honeysuckle and various grasses were commonly used to create the pattern and these were often combined with hats, fans, fences, bridges, cranes and waterfowl. These frequently had a symbolic meaning. Many patterns were asymmetrical but classical repeat patterns were also very popular.

Stencil designs including plum blossom, cloud and mist, hemp leaf and spirals.

■ ACTIVITY

In your project folder design some motifs from which you could make a stencil. Place your motifs inside a square and imagine how you could cut them out. Keep them simple. They can still be very effective if repeated.

Cut out a stencil and try it out on fabric or in your project using paint. Try repeating it in different ways. See how many patterns you can create from one simple motif.

Making a stencil

You will need a natural fibre fabric (plain weave cotton or calico are ideal), fabric paints, a stencil brush or sponge, sticky tape and an iron.

An alternative to the fabric paint is pastel dye sticks. These can be applied like an oil pastel and blended together. They can be embroidered over.

1 Stencils are traditionally cut from waxed paper but you can use thin (preferably clear) plastic or cardboard. Try rubbing a wax candle or clear nail varnish around the cut-out edges in order to make it waterproof. When

transferring your design to the paper, make sure you leave a good sized border around the design so that the paint does not smudge over the edge of the card when applied. Cut out using a craft knife. Protect the surface underneath.

2 Stretch fabric onto surface and hold down with sticky tape. If the fabric is creased iron it first. Mark on the fabric with chalk where you want the stencil to go so that it is positioned correctly. Position stencil and tape if necessary.

3 Apply paint with sponge or brush using an up and down movement only. Paint may slip under the edge of the cut-out if a sideways movement is used. Apply paint sparingly at first and build up colour gradually. Remove stencil carefully, allow to dry and iron on the back to fix colours.

Direct Application

Fabric paints can be applied with a brush to create large background areas and/or a solid effect.

Applying fabric paint with a sponge will create a textured effect. Let the first colour dry and apply a second to give added depth to your design.

Fabric crayons can give you bold lines or try using them on their side to give a textured effect and try using more than one colour. They can also be used instead of fabric paint to create your stencil design.

Fabric pens are excellent for adding clearly defined lines and fine details.

Remember to heat-set the colours when they have dried to prevent running and smudging.

■ ACTIVITY

Use coloured pencils, pens and wax crayons to create some direct application designs in your folder. This should be fun since the limitations are fewer than for other techniques. Try one out on a small piece of fabric.

IN YOUR PROJECT

▶ Mount all your samples in your project, including the stencils you used, label and evaluate.

▶ How effective are these techniques? Could you use them for your costume?

▶ Is it possible to combine any of the colouring techniques in one design? Which ones could you use in combination with the embellishment techniques?

KEY POINTS

● Designs for stencilling can be complex.

● Stencils enable you to repeat a design over and over again.

● Stencils allow you to build up a detailed pattern from a simple motif.

Adapting a Pattern

Patterns are used to create three-dimensional structures from material. Existing patterns can be adapted or new ones created. Conventional methods of marking up the pattern need to be used, so everyone can follow them.

What is a Pattern?

Making a **pattern** allows you to alter a piece of flat fabric into a three-dimensional structure for a human being.

There are several ways to approach pattern making.

Block pattern

A **block pattern** is a foundation pattern constructed to fit an average figure. In industry there is a standard block pattern for every size of a particular garment. The pattern-cutter will adapt the standard block to create the style and fashion details required by the designer.

Commercial patterns

For home dressmaking you can buy **commercial patterns** which have already been adapted to create a particular style. In school you may have some block patterns or commercial patterns but they may not be the right shape, so you may need to alter them in various ways to suit your design.

SIZE SYMBOL	8	10	12	14	16	18
HORIZONTAL MEASUREMENTS						
BUST	80	84	88	92	97	102
WAIST	58	62	66	70	75	80
HIPS	85	89	93	97	102	107
BACK WIDTH	32.4	33.4	34.4	35.4	36.6	37.8
CHEST	29.8	31.2	32.6	34	35.8	37.6
SHOULDER	11.75	12	12.25	12.5	12.8	13.1
NECK WIDTH	6.75	7	7.25	7.5	7.8	8.1
DART	5.8	6.4	7	7.6	8.2	8.8
ARMHOLE	37.5	39	40.5	42	43.5	45
VERTICAL MEASUREMENTS						
NAPE TO WAIST	38.5	39	39.5	40	40.5	41
SHOULDER TO WAIST	38.5	39	39.95	40.2	40.9	41.6
ARMHOLE DEPTH	20	20.5	21	21.5	22	22.5
WAIST TO KNEE	56	57	58	59	59.5	60
WAIST TO HIP	21	21..25	21.5	21.75	22	22.25
SLEEVE MEASUREMENTS						
LENGTH TO WRIST	55.75	56.5	57.25	58	58.5	59
TOP ARM	24.8	26.2	27.6	29	30.5	32
WRIST	15	15.5	16	16.5	17	17.5
MEASUREMENTS FOR PANTS						
BODY RISE	26.5	27	27.5	28	28.5	29
SIDE SEAM	101	102	103	104	104.5	105
FINAL KNEE WIDTH	25.8	26.4	27	27.76	28.4	29.2
FINAL HEM WIDTH	25.8	26.4	27	27.6	28.4	29.2

Copying

Find a garment at home which resembles the size and shape of your design, for example dressing gowns and T-shirts are often simple T shapes. You could then measure the garment and make your own pattern.

Remember – do not throw your pattern away. Keep it in an envelope, mounted in your project folder.

IN YOUR PROJECT

▶ Explore the different ways you could make your pattern.
▶ Ask your teacher whether there are block patterns available in school or whether you will have to adapt a commercial pattern. Show the adaptations necessary in your folder.
▶ Make a miniature model in paper.
▶ After experimenting draft your own pattern.

Modelling

▷ Make a model the right size out of newspaper. When correct draw each piece out on pattern paper.

▷ For a very complex design, designers often make up a muslin or calico sample of the garment (called a **toile**) first. For a theatrical costume the actor playing the part can try it on so that the fit can be examined and adjustments made if necessary. This allows the designer to check the design before good quality fabric is cut.

▷ Try making a miniature model from scrap paper. Roughly sketch the pattern pieces you will need for your design and then make a miniature out of scrap material. This will show you which pieces should be the same length – for example back side-seams should be the same length as front side-seams – and in which order tasks have to be carried out.

The traditional Japanese **kimono** was a very simple T-shaped garment with no pleats or darts. Although the decoration was often highly complex, the construction was simple.

A kimono is made from a set length of fabric called a tan. Kimonos were worn layer upon layer and women's often had extra material on the front sides and a neckband.

Adapting a Block Pattern

To alter a block or commercial pattern you will have to do the following:

1 Make a note of all the measurements you will need for your pattern. You could work in pairs to do this. Use the diagram as a guide to which measurements you will need.

2 Look at the blocks or commercial patterns available to you and decide which pieces you need. Make a large clear diagram of them in your project folder.

3 Use a different coloured pen or pencil and mark the alterations you will need to make on the diagram. You might need to alter any of the following – length, width, armhole length, sleeve length.

Block pattern for a simple T-shirt garment

Alterations for a simple T-shirt garment

Make back and front neck wider and drop the front.

Extend fronts to give a double-breasted effect.

Create extra flare at the sides. Make a little longer.

Make sleeve wider at cuff.

4 You now need to add **pattern markings**. Use the diagram as a guide.
Seam allowances may be included on the block you used. If not you must add them as they will allow you to sew together your garments to the original size intended. A 10 mm seam allowance is used in industry. Commercial patterns usually have a seam allowance of 15 mm.
Pattern piece = size of intended finished garment + 10 millimetre seam allowance.

5 Now you are ready to draw out the pattern on **pattern paper** using the correct measurements. Follow the same procedure you have followed in your folder. Start by drawing round the blocks on pattern paper.

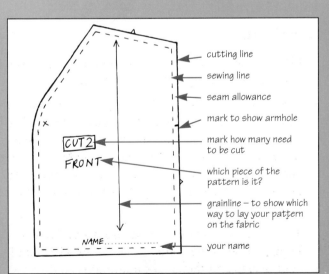

- cutting line
- sewing line
- seam allowance
- mark to show armhole
- mark how many need to be cut
- which piece of the pattern is it?
- grainline – to show which way to lay your pattern on the fabric
- your name

KEY POINTS

- A pattern will enable you to create a three-dimensional structure from a piece of flat material.
- Patterns can be adapted to create different styles.
- There are various ways to make your own pattern.
- Patterns must always have pattern markings and seam allowances.

Cutting it Out

ON STAGE

When you have completed your pattern you are ready to cut it out. Before doing this there are some things you should know about fabrics.

Grainline

The **grainline** on the pattern shows you which direction to lay your pattern piece on the fabric.

Garments are normally cut on the lengthwise grain. This is very important as a garment not cut on the straight grain will not hang properly because fabric cut on the **bias** behaves differently.

Selvedges – the edges of the roll which have been finished off by the manufacturer.

Grain lines – the weave of the fabric which is parallel to the selvedge. The straight grain can also follow the weft threads.

Warp – threads which run parallel to the selvedge.

Weft – threads which run at right angles to the warp thread.

Bias – cuts across the warp and weft threads.

■ ACTIVITY

1. Get a piece of fabric and pull it across the lengthwise grain and the crosswise grain.
▶ How does it behave?
▶ Does it stretch?

Now pull it across the bias.
▶ Does it behave differently?

2. Find out about fabrics with a **nap** or **pile**. What are they? What must you consider when cutting out a garment from a fabric which has a nap or pile?

3. What additional care is necessary when cutting out garments from fabric which has stripes, checks, large motifs or a pattern with a one-way print? Write up the results of your research in your fabric swatch book.

Detail from silk satin evening dress by Christian Lacroix, 1988

Pattern Lays

You must now place your pattern pieces on your chosen fabric in such a way that as little fabric as possible is wasted. You may need to iron the fabric and/or pattern first. Consider the following:

▷ Each piece is usually cut on the double because either it is a half-piece such as the back or because two pieces are needed (e.g. sleeves).

▷ When only one piece is needed it should be cut on single material (e.g. waistband).

Position the largest pieces first and then fit the smaller pieces around them. Pieces should be as close together as possible. There does not need to be any space between them at all. In industry this is very important as a saving of a few centimetres of fabric can reduce the total cost of a garment considerably.

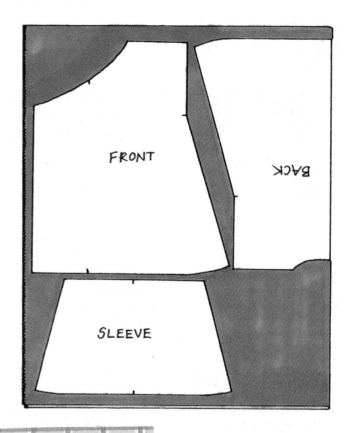

■ ACTIVITY

Experiment by arranging your pattern pieces on your chosen fabric until you find the most economical lay. Fabric comes in standard widths e.g. 115 cm and 140 cm. Which width do you think would give you the most economical lay?

IN YOUR PROJECT

▶ Draw a diagram of the final lay for your garment

KEY POINTS

● It is important to understand what the warp, weft and bias are when working with fabrics.

● The grainline on a pattern shows you which way to position the pattern piece on the fabric.

● A pattern lay is positioning your pattern pieces on your fabric in as economical a way as possible.

Putting it Together

ON STAGE

You need to prepare properly before starting to construct your design. There are many technical considerations such as choosing the correct needle and thread and ensuring you know how to use the sewing machine properly to construct even seams that will not fall apart.

The construction of theatrical garments can be quite different from the construction of everyday garments.

▷ The construction should be able to withstand quick changes between scenes.

▷ The garment may have to withstand a certain amount of wear and tear on stage depending on the part played by the wearer. Seams should therefore be very secure. The stitches should be checked frequently and a reverse stitch should be used at the beginning and end of every seam.

▷ There is no need to overlock or finish edges unless the fabric frays a lot.

▷ Seams should be pressed open and flat as you go along – this will enhance the finished quality of the garment.

▷ Zig-zag seams should be used to join knit fabrics to allow for give.

▷ Machine hems where possible.

■ ACTIVITIES

1. Revise how you use the **sewing machine**. In your project folder write down what the following are for:

▶ balance wheel
▶ presser foot
▶ feed dog
▶ foot pedal.

Thread your machine up and set it on a straight stitch. Practice sewing on a piece of scrap fabric. Try out some different stitches.

2. Re-set your machine on straight stitch. Cut two pieces of fabric to the same size and join them together using a plain seam with reverse as shown in the diagrams on page 45.

Refer to the charts below to make sure you are using the right needle, thread, and stitch length and width.

3. Mount your test pieces in your project folder and explain what the reverse stitches are for.

4. Make a flow diagram of the construction of your garment. Use the diagrams on the next page to help you.

What machine needle should you use?

Fabric	Needle size	Needle type
Lightweight-cotton lawn, silk, lace	11 (80 metric size)	Sharp point
Medium weight – polycottons, cottons, e.g. needlecord, poplin, and prints	14 (90 metric size)	Sharp point
Heavyweight – woollens, cottons, e.g. corduroy, velvet, terry-towelling, gabardine	16 (100 metric size)	Sharp point
All knitted fabrics	According to weight	Ball point

Your thread should match the fabric in thickness and fibre type.

Getting it stitched up

Here is a rough guide to help you work out what stitch length, stitch width and needle position you need:

	Stitch length (mm)	Stitch width (mm)	Needle position
Straight stitch	2 ½	0	Centre
Gathering	4	0	Centre
Zig-zag	2	3-4	Centre

The finer the fabric the shorter the stitch e.g.
▶ For acetate lining – 2mm
▶ For medium weight – 3mm
▶ For quilting and thicker fabric – 4mm +

Constructing a seam

1 Pin two pieces of fabric together.

2 Use the marked guidelines on the machine to sew down line with machine and reverse at each end.

3 Press the seam open and flat with an iron.

Final construction

1 Apply stencil designs to the back and front of the garment. Allow to dry. Press the back with an iron in order to fix the colour.

2 Join front shoulders to back. Remember to put right sides together.

3 Press open shoulder seams with an iron.
Stitch sleeves to garment before side seams and sleeve seams are stitched. Close garment right sides together and stitch sleeve and side seam.

4 Hem edges twice. Press up and stitch on the machine – cuffs, fronts, back neck and around the bottom.

5 Turn right side out. Pin, tack and sew on trim around the edges.

Planning the Making/Testing and Evaluating

You will be presenting your ideas at a production meeting at which the theatre director and other people involved in the production will be present. Some careful planning and preparation will be needed to ensure you have all of the following ready on time:

▷ *initial ideas for costumes or stage set fabrics*

▷ *test pieces*

▷ *a sample costume for one of the main characters, or samples of fabrics for the stage set*

▷ *ideas for the stage set.*

Planning Check-list

▷ Time: how long will each task take? Which task do you think will take the longest? How much time do you have to complete the garment?

▷ Will you be able to obtain appropriate materials in time?

▷ What tools and equipment will you need?

▷ How can you minimise waste of time and materials?

▷ How can you ensure that your finished garment is of a good quality?

Have you practised all the techniques you are going to need? If not it is a good idea to do so as this will enhance the quality of the final item.

Prepare Stencil

Apply Stencil

Stitch Shoulder

Time Management

You must be aware of how long it is taking you to complete each task and how long you have left. You may have over or under-estimated the time available, in which case you may have to adjust your plan or your final design.

Quality Control

In industry there is always a system of **quality control**. This involves checking the quality of the item being made at various stages of its production.

It is a good idea for you to check your making as you go along and record it alongside your production plan.

Week	Activity	Tools/ Equipment	Quality control
1	Cut out Prepare stencils	Scissors, tailors chalk, paper, craft knife, pencil	Found it difficult to keep the fabric flat when pinning
2	Apply stencil designs to garment pieces. Iron back to fix colours	Tape, stencils, clean surface, sponges, brushes, fabric paints	
3	Join front shoulders to back and press open and flat.		

IN YOUR PROJECT

▶ You will almost certainly encounter problems during manufacture and you may have to change your plan, design, materials and/or equipment in order to overcome them.

▶ Keep a diary in your project folder and record problems you encounter each week and how you overcome them.

Final Testing

You could test each other's work by holding your own production meetings in class in groups of four or five. Present your work to the group and discuss your ideas with them. The outcomes of the meeting need to be recorded in some way. Try drawing up a chart similar to the one shown in which comments and ideas can be recorded.

Remember to make positive comments about each others work and suggest constructive improvements.

Turning Japanese ?

Perhaps the most memorable part of last night's opening night of a new production of *The Mikado* was the stunning costumes and stage-set. A dazzling spectacle of rich, vivid purple and gold costumes and fabric screens derived from traditional Japanese patterns and motifs instantly transported the audience into nineteenth century Japan.

KEY POINTS

- Planning the production of your product is very important.
- Thorough planning will lead to a 'quality' product.
- Considering time limitations is necessary if you are to complete your project successfully.

Criteria	Make comments on
Interpretation of the theme	Your overall view of the entire project. • How strong is the Japanese theme and is it consistent throughout the project? • How would it appear during a performance of The Mikado?
Colour ideas and co-ordination	Are they appropriate for the theme? • Do colours chosen for costumes reflect the characters? • Do colours for sets create the right atmosphere?
Initial ideas for costumes or fabrics for the stage set	Overall use of shape, style, colour, etc. • What will they look like from a distance when on stage? • Are they appropriate for the atmosphere of the musical and the character?
Test pieces	Overall use of colour, design, etc. • Could any of the colours/techniques be developed more for the final designs?
Sample costume or fabrics	Overall colour, shape, style, details and techniques. • What will it look like on stage with the sets. • Are they appropriate for the theme and the storyline? • Do they create the right atmosphere?

The final test – what the theatre critics say...!

Final Evaluation

Check your work against the requirements of the original specification, e.g. in terms of the function, aesthetics, safety, cost and materials.

Assess the quality of design (i.e. the use of theme, colour, shape, style, pattern) and the quality of manufacture (i.e. the finishing off of seams, top-stitching, techniques, dyeing/painting, etc.).

Make sure you write up your final evaluation in your design folder.

Examination Questions (1)

Before spending about one and a half hours attempting the following questions you will need to do some preliminary research into:

▷ *images and colours associated with the seaside*
▷ *how colour and texture can be used in clothing and living spaces to create different moods.*

Design brief

A small manufacturer has asked you to design for one of the following:

1. Soft furnishings for seaside holiday cottages. The items you design will be manufactured in small quantities for a number of cottages.

2. A small collection of holiday clothing and accessories to be worn at the seaside. The clothing items will be manufactured in small quantities to be sold in selected shops.

▷ The products you design are to be decorated with applique.
▷ The applique designs are to be based on the colours and shapes associated with the seaside.

You must choose either 1 or 2 and then relate all your answers to the following questions to the type of product you have selected.

1. **This question is about designing.** *(Total 33 marks.)* See pages 8-9, 12-13, 28-29, 30-31.

(a) Write down three things you will need to know or find out about before you can start designing products in your range.

Give the reason why you think that each factor is important. *(6 marks)*

(b) Give three sources of information you could use for your design ideas. *(3 marks)*

(c) Sketch an initial idea for two products in your range. One of these ideas is to be developed into a final design. *(4 marks)*

(d) Use drawings, labelling and notes to present a final design for your product. Show clearly what the applique decoration looks like and where it is to be placed. Marks will be awarded for:

▷ the applique design *(6 marks)*
▷ the colours *(3 marks)*
▷ the design for the product. *(3 marks)*
▷ the presentation of the design. *(5 marks)*

(e) Explain how the colours you have chosen for your product create an image or a mood. *(3 marks)*

2. This question is about the modification of your appliqué design. *(Total 20 marks.)* See pages 32-33, 38-39.

(a)   The manufacturer wishes to print some fabric for some of the products in your range. Use notes and sketches to show how you could modify your appliqué design to make a motif suitable for printing.
(6 marks)

(b)   Show how the motif could be arranged to make an interesting border print.   *(4 marks)*

(c)   Use notes and labelled diagrams to show how you could print your border on to a length of fabric.   *(10 marks)*

3. This question is about the making of a sample product. *(Total 28 marks.)* See pages 32-35, 40-45.

(a)   (i) Draw and name the stitch you would use to attach the appliqué to the main fabric used for the product.   *(4 marks)*
(ii) Give two reasons why you chose this stitch.   *(2 marks)*

(b)   Part of the appliqué may be made from a slippery fabric. Explain how you would ensure that this fabric is firm enough to give a good result.   *(3 marks)*

(c)   Give two ways in which you can introduce texture into the design for your appliqué.   *(2 marks)*

(d)   (i) Give two ways in which you could make a pattern for your product.   *(2 marks)*
(ii) Explain how you could check your pattern before cutting out the final fabric.   *(2 marks)*
(iii) Give three reasons why it is advisable to check the pattern before cutting out the final fabric. *(3 marks)*

(e)   (i) Explain what is meant by 'straight grain'.   *(2 marks)*
(ii) Why is it important to place the pattern pieces for your product on the straight grain of the fabric?   *(2 marks)*

(f)   Use labelled diagrams to show how you would make a seam to join sections of your product   *(6 marks)*

4. This question is about industrial manufacture of your product. *(Total 10 marks.)* See pages 38-39, 46-47.

(a)   Your product is to be manufactured in limited quantities.
(i) Which manufacturing system would you recommend?   *(1 mark)*
(ii) Give two reasons for your choice of manufacturing system?   *(2 marks)*

(b)   Give two ways in which a spreadsheet would be useful when manufacturing your product in quantity.   *(2 marks)*

(c)   Give two checks that a manufacturer might make during the making of your product to ensure that it is of the highest quality.   *(2 marks)*

(d)   Explain why a manufacturer should plan pattern lays carefully.   *(3 marks)*

Project Two: Introduction

Textiles play an essential role in the area of sports and leisurewear. As a freelance designer you have been asked by a local company to develop a new range of bags and garments which can be used in very different ways.

Ergonomics (page 54)

Fabric Constructions (page 62)

Construction Methods (page 70)

GETout is a well-established company which specialises in the production of garments and accessories for a wide range of outdoor activities such as camping, walking and cycling.

To begin with we planned to revitalise our business by developing a new co-ordinated product range of small containers/bags and outside garments with special pockets for such activities. However our market research has shown that there are new uses for our products within the typical family.

We therefore need to re-think our designs drastically, and need some new ideas to take us forward. We are therefore hoping you will be able to design a highly adaptable bag, rucksack or carrier and/or garment which will appeal to our potential family market.

1 —

Clarifying the Brief

Carefully read the letter on the left.

Make a list of all the things the client expects you to do.

Are you going to concentrate on the bag or the garment?

■ ACTIVITY

Start to look through catalogues, magazines and in shops, etc., to find out what type of products are already on the market.

Collect pictures and make sketches. Note down materials and trimmings used and cost.

What we need to see are:

*   a statement of the range of different situations in which the bag or garment could be used, and what it will be able to carry.
*   sketches to show colour variations and adaptable sections that could be added or taken off according to use
*   a prototype model of one container or garment, showing how it can be adapted.
*   a name and logo for our new product range to help give it a strong identity in the mind of the public.

Remember that the adaptability of the product is very important, and the key to our success.

I look forward to discussing your ideas with you in the near future.

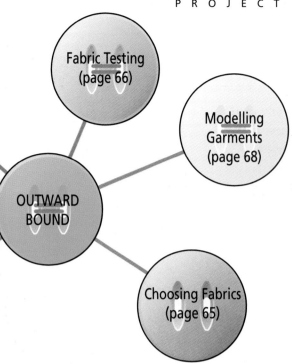

Designing for a Market

Designers must design for people's needs. As different people have different needs designers must have in mind a clearly defined group of people who have similar needs. This group is called a **target market**.

Some target markets may be very broad, such as adults aged 25-40 years, or they may be quite small, such as very young children with specific disabilities.

GETout's research helped them build up the following picture of their target market, which proved to be very broad.

MARKET RESEARCH PROFILE

*The GETout Family
are Outward Bound...*

Dad has developed an interest in mountain biking and photography while Mum wants something to take her kit in for her T'ai chi course every Thursday evening.

Sarah, who insists on being known as Serena, is in her mid teens and needs a bag for a disco sleep-over, which will hold just about anything (and she's not saying what).

Meanwhile Brian, her older teenager brother wants to GETout to a rock concert at Hestonbury, and needs something to store everything he'll need to survive for three days.

They also need some outdoor wear which will keep them warm and dry, and will help them carry the various things they need. Again something that Mum and Dad can share, or Serena and Brian can fight over whose turn it is to use, would be ideal!

KEY POINTS

- Designers design for a specific group of people called a target market.
- To find out about a market, designers and manufacturers often carry out market research.

COLSTON'S GIRLS' SCHOOL

Carry on Carrying

There is a limit to how much our hands and arms can hold. People have always used their ingenuity to find better and easier ways of carrying things.

What different ways can you think of for transporting your possessions, safely and comfortably?

How often have you tried to carry a lot of small objects around at once, only to discover you keep dropping things? There are a wide variety of bags, boxes and other containers that can help make it easier to carry things around.

■ ACTIVITY

Study the containers on this page.
▶ What things is each normally used to carry?
▶ What completely different things could they hold?
▶ When might someone need to use each container?
▶ What materials might each container be made from?

Manual transport in Kenya

Backpack with headband in Nepal

First Thoughts

▷ How many outward bound activities can you think of?

▷ What do people need to carry with them when participating in these activities? Which of these items do you consider to be really vital?

▷ What kind of clothes would they wear?

▷ What sort of image do these activities have?

▷ Do you know any shops or well-known companies which specialise in this area?

▷ How might one basic design be adapted to make it suitable for different uses?

In your design folder, brainstorm your initial thoughts and ideas.

Logos are essential to a strong brand image especially in sportswear.

elastic strip can be used to hold extra items.

protective high collar. warm, 'breathable' fabric. Clear pocket for map.

Comfortable stretch top incorporating logo strip!

covered zip pocket

piping made from reflective fabric to aid night safety.

smaller 'bum' bag can be zipped to an extra section for different uses.

All straps are adjustable.

Unisex jacket with windproof/waterproof details e.g. covered front zip, flap pockets and tabs to tighten cuffs.

Ergonomic Investigation

You will need to carry out some detailed research into the various elements of your project. You will need to find out more about the ergonomic requirements of your product and target market. Evaluating an existing product will help you understand a lot more about what the problems are.

Ergonomics

Ergonomics is the study of the way in which a product, the user and the environment affect each other. Examples of designs which have not taken ergonomic considerations into account are a jacket for mountain climbing which will not provide protection against very bad weather and a rucksack which is difficult to put on and take off.

Make sure you think carefully about the health, safety, convenience and comfort of the user when analysing, evaluating or developing design ideas.

■ ACTIVITY

Make an ergonomic study of someone you know either trying to carry a number of items in a rucksack or trying to put on or take off a garment which is complicated to do up.

You will need to take some overall measurements of the person and the product, watch them use it and ask them some questions.

► Are their arms long enough?
► Are their hands big enough?
► Can they pick up and carry the loaded rucksack with ease?
► Are any pockets easy to open and close? Are they too big or small?
► Are any straps long and wide enough, and easy to adjust?
► Is it easy to clean and mantain?
► Does the user like the colours, shapes, patterns and textures?
► Do they enjoy using it?

Design Disassembly

Find some different types of containers or garments and make sketches of them in your project folder – back, front and sides. Examine the insides for extra compartments. Enlarge some of the finer details if necessary, e.g. fastenings, logos, decorative stitching, etc.

Alternatively, disassemble an appropriate garment. Examine it carefully and draw diagrams of all the pattern pieces needed to make it. Consider how well it performs in terms of use, safety, adjustability and weatherproofness.

Your conclusions will need to focus on the following questions.

▷ Do you think it is a successful design? Is it fit for its intended purpose?
▷ What are its good and bad points?
▷ Is it ergonomically sound?
▷ Can you suggest any improvements?

Safety

The design of a rucksack must be considered carefully to ensure the well-being and safety of the wearer.

Most of the weight is concentrated on the hips but a certain amount has to be carried through the shoulder straps in order to hold the pack next to the back for stability. This keeps the weight as close as possible to the centre of gravity, otherwise the wearer could easily topple over.

Cyclops Back System

Extendible lid strap

Top tension strap

Top tension adjusters

Ventilation channel

Compression strap sewen right through the frame

Advent fabric for comfort against skin

Windclips to stop excess straps flapping in wind (not visible)

Polypex reinforced hipbelt sewen through the frame

Cynch straps for stability at base

Dual adjust bergbuckle (alloys positioning in either direction)

Adjustability

The distance from shoulders to hips varies from person to person. To ensure that a rucksack fits the back as snugly as possible the back-straps are usually adjustable in length. This means that it can be altered:

▷ to fit a growing body
▷ to fit people of different sizes
▷ to allow for different types of clothing worn in the summer and winter.

Fixed length rucksacks have appeal to some people because of their stability, strength and ease of fit.

Against the elements

How do you make something waterproof? Is using waterproof fabric enough?

▷ Which fastenings are waterproof?
▷ Which designs are most likely to keep out water?
▷ Where is the best place to put seams and fastenings?
▷ How could you make the design more waterproof?

Covered, zipped pockets protect the contents from the elements.

Elasticated waist and hems to stop water entering.

Double stitched seams with rubber backing to prevent leaking.

High performanc fabric with a warmer thermal lining.

DISASSEMBLY CHECKLIST

✔ Describe the sort of person who might wear/carry it and on what sort of occasion.
✔ Where are the seams, top stitching, openings?
✔ Describe the fibres and fabrics used. How might they have been printed or dyed?
✔ Have any trimmings been used effectively?
✔ Have any fastenings been well chosen and placed?
✔ Have any other materials been used, particularly on the inside? If so, why, and how effectively?
✔ Where are the labels and what information is on them? Do they provide enough information?
✔ Is there a brand name or a manufacturer's name?

Fibres to Fabrics

Textile designers need to have a wider knowledge and understanding of different fibres and fabrics and how they are constructed.

woollen fibres taken from sheep

spun into yarns

made into fabric

manufactured into textile items

woven skirt

knitted jumper

woven   knitted

Fibres to Fabrics

FABRIC

is

WOVEN   KNITTED

from

YARNS (filament/staple)

which are

SPUN

from

FIBRES

NATURAL   MAN MADE

Animals

silk - worms
wool - sheep

cotton - plant
linen - flax

Plants

cellulose - Viscose
wood pulp - Acetate

Regenerated Cellulose

oil and coal - Nylon
compounds obtained - Polyester
from coal
oil   - Acrylic

Synthetic

■ ACTIVITIES

1. Carry out an investigation into the spinning process for:
▶ a natural fibre such as wool or cotton
▶ a regenerated cellulose fibre such as viscose or acetate
▶ a synthetic fibre such as polyester or acrylic.

Write up your findings in your fabric swatch book.

2. How many items can you find at home and at school that have been made from cotton? List them in your fabric swatch book and describe the characteristics of the cotton fabric used for each.

Make similar notes for other fibres such as polyester, wool, acrylic and nylon.

The Properties of Fibres

The way a fibre is made into a yarn or the yarn is made into a fabric will affect the final properties of the fabric. For example:

▷ The thickness or weight of a fabric can be altered by using different thicknesses of yarn.
▷ The final texture of a fabric can be altered by adding texture to the yarns it is made from.

There are many different weaves used to make fabrics, e.g.:

▷ twill weave used to make denim.
▷ pile weave used to make corduroy and velvet.

The way in which a fabric is constructed will affect its properties.

A knitted structure will usually give fabric different properties to a woven one.

Further properties can be given to a fabric by adding different finishes, for example waterproof finish.

Fabrics may therefore have different properties even though they have the same fibre content.

Yarns

Yarns can be made from staple fibres which are short and twisted together to form a yarn or they can be made from filament fibres which are already long and ready for twisting. All natural fibres are staple apart from silk. Silk is the only natural filament yarn: the rest are man-made.

Fibre property chart

A fibre property chart provides a general guide to fabric properties.

	natural fibres				man-made fibres				
	Silk	Wool	Linen	Cotton	Acetate	Acrylic	Nylon	Polyester	Viscose
Abrasion resistance	✳✳	✳✳	✳✳	✳✳		✳✳	✳✳✳	✳✳✳	✳
Absorbency	✳✳✳	✳✳✳	✳✳	✳✳	✳✳				✳✳✳
Elasticity	✳✳	✳✳✳	✳		✳✳	✳✳	✳✳✳	✳✳✳	✳✳
Flame resistance	✳✳✳	✳✳✳	✳	✳	✳		✳✳	✳✳	✳
Insulation	✳✳✳	✳✳✳	✳	✳	✳✳	✳✳	✳✳	✳✳	✳
Mothproof	✳	✳	✳✳	✳✳	✳✳	✳✳	✳✳	✳✳	✳✳
Mildew resistance	✳	✳			✳✳✳	✳✳✳	✳✳✳	✳✳✳	✳
Resistance to acids	✳	✳✳	✳✳	✳✳	✳✳	✳✳✳		✳✳	✳
Resistance to alkalis	✳	✳✳	✳✳	✳✳✳		✳✳	✳✳	✳✳	✳✳
Resistance to damage by bleach	✳	✳	✳✳	✳✳	✳	✳	✳✳	✳✳✳	
Resistance to damage by sunlight	✳	✳	✳✳	✳✳	✳✳	✳✳	✳✳✳	✳✳	✳
Static electricity	✳✳✳	✳✳✳	✳✳✳	✳✳✳	✳	✳	✳	✳	
Tensile strength	✳✳✳	✳	✳✳	✳✳	✳	✳	✳✳✳	✳✳✳	✳✳
Thermal conductivity	✳	✳	✳✳✳	✳✳✳	✳	✳	✳	✳	✳✳
Thermoplasticity	I	I	I	I	✳✳	✳✳	✳✳	✳✳✳	I

IN YOUR PROJECT

► Which fibres and fabrics would be most suitable for:
– your container?
– your garment?
► Why are they suitable?

KEY POINTS

● Fibres can be natural, regenerated cellulose or synthetic.
● Fibres are spun into yarns.
● Yarns can be given added texture by twisting, crimping and looping.
● Fabric construction methods can affect the appearance, texture and properties of the fabric.
● Fabrics can be given special finishes to make them more useful.

Specification/Container Design Development

The next stage in developing your designs for GETout is to focus on the possibilities and limitations by preparing a design specification, and then to develop some of your first thoughts into more detailed design ideas.

Review all the information you have gathered during your research and investigation and make the following decisions.

Who is it for?

Make a clear statement of the needs of the people you are designing for.

What will it contain?

List the items it may reasonably need to accommodate.

Materials

What qualities will the materials need to have in terms of strength, durability, weather-proofing, etc.

Size

You can only make an estimate at this stage. Try measuring some of the items that are most likely to be placed in the bag.

Appearance

What sorts of colours, textures and patterns will be most appropriate?

Specification

My container is for...
- It is for carrying...
- It will be no smaller than...
- It will be no bigger than...
- The materials will need to be...
- It must be comfortable to carry and convenient to use, i.e. ergonomically designed
- The shape and colours will....

Embroidered logo

plan of the inside of the bag.

Logo embossed onto metal press stud

Double top stitch detail increases durability and creates a design feature

Straps are stitched down to create loops

Zip section allows the ruc sac straps to be stored neatly.

Logo zip pull

Draw string bag with drawstring top for ease of entry. Waterproof fabric is used for the protective top flap.

Concealed zips are used because they repel wind and water.

Logo used as a fabric print.

Developing your Ideas

Read the sections on Fabric Construction and Choosing and Testing Fabrics which follow on pages 62 to 67. You will need to do some of the activities. Make notes in your design folder as your ideas for the GETout bag or garment develop.

As you develop your ideas keep the following questions in mind.

Fibres to fabric construction

▷ Which **fabrics** will be the most hard-wearing?
▷ Are knitted fabrics as strong as woven ones?
▷ Do you need a fabric which will be able to stretch?
▷ Which will look acceptable to both a teenager and an adult?
▷ Which would make the best combination of style and durability?

Choosing and testing fabrics

▷ What properties will the fabric you choose need to have?
▷ What special finishes could be applied to help make the bag hardwearing and look good at the same time?

Ergonomics

You should also look back at page 54 which asked you to evaluate an existing rucksack from an ergonomic point of view. As you develop your ideas you will need to think about the **ergonomics** of your design. Consider the environment in which your container will be used.

▷ Will it be wet?
▷ Will the user need to carry anything bulky or heavy during the activity?
▷ How many different ways can the container be carried? For example a cyclist will not be able to carry anything by hand or anything very bulky.
▷ How can adjustability be provided?
▷ What methods of carrying would be best?
▷ Which fastenings would be most appropriate?

Detailed Development

After producing some ideas evaluate them. Decide which may be the most promising, and make a note of why.

Develop one or two by focusing on them in more detail. At this next stage features such as size, fastenings and pockets should be considered.

visible zips can be made weatherproof by adding a strip of fabric behind.

A bold logo creates a strong brand image.

Double stitching improves the strength of a seam.

velcro strips

elastic loops

Adjustable straps can hold camping, cycling and sports equipment.

Adjustable straps can be used to attach the bag to a bike as a pannier.

Top flap is made from a waterproof fabric to protect the contents.

Initial idea developed

The bag is tightened with cord grips.

Strong metal snap-hook fastener

Elastic strip holds fragile objects

Xtra space is created with zip-on section.

Double zip section allows quick, easy access.

The use of florescent fabric on the bag will improve night safety.

Press studs used to close the bag.

Specification/Garment Design Development

If you are developing ideas for a garment with special storage pockets to present to GETout, the next stage is to focus on the possibilities and limitations by preparing a design specification, and then to develop some of your first thoughts into more detailed design ideas.

How long do fashions last?

Specification

You need to focus on the possibilities and limitations for your garment by preparing a **design specification**.

The garment will have to be suitable for the activities identified as appropriate to the target market. It will also need to reflect current trends in the use of fabrics, styles and colours for leisurewear.

Review all the information you have gathered during your research and investigation and make the following decisions.

Many sports garments/ accessories have become desirable fashion items in themselves. Can you think of any?

Who is it for?
Make a clear statement of the needs of the people you are designing for.

What will it contain?
List the items the wearer may want to carry.

Materials
What qualities will the materials need to have in terms of strength, durability, weather-proofing, etc.

Size
You can only make an estimate at this stage. Try measuring some of the items that are most likely to be placed in it.

Appearance
What sorts of colours, textures and patterns will be most appropriate?

Specification Checklist

- ✔ My garment is for...
- ✔ It is for carrying...
- ✔ The materials will need to be...
- ✔ It must be comfortable to wear and convenient to use.
- ✔ The shape and colours will...

The Influence of Fashion

The market for sports and leisurewear has expanded rapidly in the twentieth century.

Developments in industry and technology have given people more time in which to pursue leisure activities. The market includes all sorts of woven and knitted specialised sportswear and casual garments to suit many different occasions.

Such garments and the accessories that go with them are influenced to some extent by the fashions of the time.

■ ACTIVITY

Carry out an investigation into the growth of the leisure market in this century.
- ▶ Has the growth of this area affected the way we dress generally?
- ▶ How has the development of textile technology affected the range of garments on offer to the public? Think about fabric construction as well as fibre development.

Developing Design Ideas

You will need to develop a series of ideas for your garment. Remember that the way it can be adapted to help carry different items must be a key element in the design. Maybe some of your shapes, colours and patterns could be based on ideas taken from historical designs.

If your design is going to be successful you will need to know more about

▷ how fabrics are constructed (see pages 62 to 64)
▷ how to choose the right fabric by analysing its characteristics and properties (see pages 65 to 67).
▷ how to make mock-ups and patterns (see pages 68 to 69).

Presentation

GETout will want to see all your ideas so the way you present your sketches will be very important.

You do not have to be brilliant at drawing people to present garment ideas effectively. You can draw garments and accessories on their own in diagrammatic form.

Experiment to find a way that suits you and enables you to get ideas down on paper quickly and effectively.

You may sketch or trace the outline of a figure from a photograph onto which you can add garments, details and accessories etc. Make yourself a collection of outlines which you can keep in your folder to use.

What are you going to use to render your sketches? Coloured pencils can be very effective. You can also try water-colours, inks and different coloured pens.

■ ACTIVITY

Practise creating textures using different media. Try the following:
▶ rough tweed
▶ satin
▶ woolly jumper
▶ nylon shell suit.

Keeping Warm and Dry

You will need to think about your garment's ability to protect against the elements. Most outdoor jackets attain a high degree of water repellence. Most seams are taped so that they do not leak.

Size
Jackets should be generously sized to allow freedom of movement and allow moisture to evaporate.

Zips
A storm flap, held down by velcro or a press stud will prevent leakage through zip fastenings. Dual zips may be used with a fleece lining to make the garment more versatile.

Length
A longer jacket offers better protection but shorter jackets may be necessary for some active sports.

Hoods
Whether attached, detachable or foldaway they should be large enough to protect against the elements but not restrict vision.

Cuffs
Cuffs should close tightly, using elastic or Velcro to protect against wind and rain

Drawstrings
Drawstrings are usually placed at the hem, waist or hood to stop wind or rain entering. Springlocks make these fastenings easier to use.

Pockets
Pockets may need to be large enough to enable access by someone wearing gloves. Access to some pockets must be possible without undoing the main zip.

Knitted

Herringbone

Woven

An Outfit For The GETout Family

Embroidered badge

Detachable hood can be stored in zipped section of the collar

Detachable sleeves gives the wearer flexibility

Elasticated cuffs and drawstring hem protect the wearer from the elements

covered zip pocket

Cotton/viscose mix fabrics are hardwearing and easy to clean

The yolks are made of a printed cotton coated man plastic.

The jacket has a layer of wadding between the outer shell and lining, this helps with warmth.

Loose fitting trousers with elastic waistband

Fabric Construction (1)

Most fabrics are constructed by weaving or knitting yarns together. Some are bonded together or felted.

How a fabric behaves depends on the structure of the fabric, the structure of the yarn and the finishes applied.

Get Weaving

Weaving involves the crossing of two sets of **yarns** (the **warp** and the **weft**), over and under each other. Fabrics were traditionally produced on a hand-operated loom. Modern machine operated looms are much more complex and controlled by computer.

Plain weave
A plain weave is the simplest weave: the weft threads pass over and under alternate warp threads. In other weaves the weft is passed over or under more than one warp thread.

Satin weave
In satin the weft goes under several and over one. Because there is more thread lying on the surface the fabric looks lustrous and glossy. ▶

◀ Twill weave
Twill which creates a diagonal pattern on the fabric surface is used to produce strong close weaves such as drill for aprons and overalls and denim used for jeans.

Terry/velvet weave
Some complex weaves such as terry and velvet result in raised or looped surfaces. These are woven by extra warp threads making the loops on a plain weave. The loops increase the surface area of the fabric so that it can absorb more water.

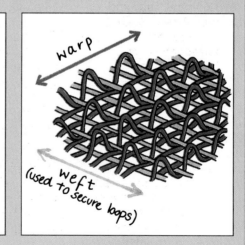

Knitting

Knitting has a looped structure. This is unlike weaving where the yarns remain almost straight.

Weft knitting
The yarn runs across the fabric making loops with the row underneath.

Single jersey
Hand knitters call this stocking stitch (one row plain one row purl). It is often used for T-shirts.

Ribknit or ribbing
Both sides look the same with the ribs of plain and purl running up the fabric. It is very elastic and snaps back into shape very quickly after being stretched. It is used for waistbands, cuffs and neckbands on sweatshirts, tracksuits and woven jackets.

Double jersey
Made on a 'double bed machine' that uses two sets of needles, each with its own supply of yarn. This means that it may be much thicker than single jersey, a firm fabric that lies flat and has much less stretch than single jersey.

Warp knitting
Cannot be produced by hand-knitting like weft fabrics. In warp-knitted fabrics the yarns run 'up' the fabric like the warp yarns in weaving. It can be firm, like a woven fabric or slightly stretchy. It keeps its shape well so it can be used to make very fine, lightweight fabrics and most warp knits do not ladder.

What are the differences between woven and knitted fabrics?
- Knits have a looped structure and wovens do not.
- Knits do not fray at the edge the way wovens do although they may run, i.e. the loops may unravel.
- Knits (particularly wefts) have much more stretch (although wovens have a little more stretch in the bias). Stretch allows us to move with comfort which is why knits are preferred for close fitting casual garments, underwear, tights and sportswear.
- Knits are usually more open so that air can pass thorough them easily. This is useful on a hot day but not so good on a cold, windy day.

Non-woven Fabrics

Bonded fabrics
Non-woven fabric is generally made from 'webs' or 'batts' of fibre held together and strengthened by bonding. This is achieved by using a resin adhesive, needle-punching, or stitch bonding with thread. The choice is determined by the method of manufacture.

Early non-wovens were unattractive in appearance, handle and drape. It is still difficult to achieve the characteristics of knitted and woven structures. Their advantage is that they are cheaper to manufacture.

As well as being used for interlinings and insulation in clothing, non-wovens are used in disposable hygenic and absorbant products. Other uses include resin-free liners for floppy disks and artificial leathers.

Felting
Felting is an older way of constructing a non-woven fabric. It is made from a combination of moisture, heat, friction and pressure. It is traditionally made from wool but today is more often made from synthetic or recycled yarns. Most carpet underlay is synthetic felt, and it has become popular as a craft material for creative collages and for making hats.

KEY POINTS
- Yarns are woven, knitted or bonded into fabrics.
- Woven and knit structures give different properties to the final fabric.
- Wovens do not stretch as much as knits.
- Bonded fabrics can be produced cheaply but are not as strong as woven and knitted fabrics.

Using adhesive, under pressure and heat, the fibres are bonded together.

Fabric Construction (2)

Something's burning...

Your teacher must supervise you doing the following activity. You will need some fabric samples. Set up a controlled test in which you burn each sample. Use the table below to identify which fibres each is made from.

Disassembly and Evaluation of Fabrics

Investigate some samples of woven, knitted and bonded fabrics. Use a magnifying lens to help you disassemble the fabrics. Record your findings in your fabric swatch book.

▷ Describe the appearance and feel of the sample.
▷ Tease out some of the yarns and examine them. Have they been texturised in any way?
▷ Untwist the yarn carefully. Is it made up of fine fibres? How many fibres make up the yarn? Are the fibres staple or filament?
▷ Is the fabric woven or knitted?
▷ Can you identify the type of weave or knit?
▷ Draw a diagram of the fabric structure

	Burning/flame	Smell	Ash or residue
Cotton/viscose	Burns readily and quickly Yellow flame	Burning paper	Greyish white ash
Linen	Burns readily Yellowy orange flame	Bonfire smell of burning grass	Grey ash
Wool	Smoulders; burns slowly Fibre burns inside the flame. Does not flare up.	Burning feathers or human hair	Black bead which crushes easily when cold
Silk	Small brittle beads Fibre burns inside the flame. Does not flare up.	Burning feathers or human hair	Burns to ash
Acetate	Slower than viscose	Vinegar smell	Melts to a hard shiny black bead
Nylon	Not flammable i.e. it shrinks away from heat of flame, melting and dripping Yellow flame	Strong celery smell	Light coloured fawn or white hard round bead
Polyester	Difficult to ignite. Melts and shrinks from the flame. Hard beaded edges Luminous red or yellow flame	Strong	Hard round bead, darker than nylon.
Acrylic	Burns then melts Luminous reddish flame	Aromatic odour	Hard black bead of irregular shape

■ ACTIVITY

Carry out an investigation into the fibres and fabrics used for sports and leisurewear and present your findings in a chart as shown below.

Use the properties chart on page 57 and the information on page 63 to say why each fabric was chosen for that particular end use.

Item	Uses	Construction	Fibre content	Reasons for use
Sweat shirt	Casual wear – worn as a tracksuit top	Knitted fabric brushed on one side. Ribbed cuffs	100% cotton	Cotton is soft, comfortable and absorbent – therefore good for sports. Knitted fabric stretches with the body during wear – good for sports. Brushed inside creates extra bulk – traps air, therefore added warmth.

Choosing Fabrics

It is important to choose fabrics which are fit for their intended purpose.

Different fabrics have different properties and characteristics.

Testing the handle of apparel fabrics

Properties of Fabrics

How will the fabric behave during use?

Abrasion resistance	Windproof	Resilient
Tensile strength	Thermal insulator	Crease-resistant
Washable	Thermal conductor	Non-flammable
Boilable	Absorbent	Thermoplastic
Non-fade	Waterproof	Sunlight resistant
Colour-fast	Showerproof	Mothproof
Non-shrink	Non-irritant	Rot-proof
Drip-dry	Elastic	Resistant to bleach/chemicals

Discuss in groups what the above properties mean.

Characteristics of Fabrics

How will the fabric look, feel, and behave?

Drape	Loosely/tightly made
Thickness	Snagging
Weight	Dimensional stability
Texture	Fraying
Transparency	Hole recovery
Colour and pattern	

Write down all the words you can think of to describe the possible texture of fabrics.

■ ACTIVITY

What can you find out about the following finishes: water-proof, showerproof, shrink resist, non-shrink, mothproofing, anti-static and rubberising? List the advantages of these finishes in your fabric swatch book.

Fabric Finishes

Some finishes such as bleaching are used to improve the appearance of fabrics.

Performance finishes

These are used to give a fabric useful properties or to enhance properties it already has.

Stain and soil resistance

Fabric is finished using a mixture of silicone and fluorine. This prevents grease and dirt entering the fabric which is very useful for carpets and upholstery.

Flame retardance

The flammability performance of fabrics is an essential consideration. The aim is to produce an inexpensive, durable finish which will not compromise handling, strength or wearing properties.

Some finishes work by making the fabric unable to produce fuel vapours that normally feed the flame. Others produce vapours which help suppress the flame. The most widely used finishes are 'Proban' and 'Durovatex'.

Crease resistance

Cotton, linen and rayon crease badly. They can now be treated using a process which involves combining the fibres with a resin. Sometimes, however, this reduces strength and resistance to abrasion.

Modern finishes have greatly improved characteristics. In particular synthetic fibres show very good crease recovery. They are thermoplastic which means they become soft and pliable at higher temperatures. Nylon, polyester and acrylics are thermoplastic. This means that they can be heat-set into shape and given pleats which are permanent.

Brushing

Fabrics can be brushed by passing them through a large rotating brush. This raises the surface of the fabric which means it can trap air and keep the body warmer.

OUTWARD BOUND

fabrics

Testing Fabrics

Fabrics need to be tested rigorously before a product goes into production to ensure that they will be fit for their intended purpose. There are some simple tests you can do, under supervision, at home or at school. Remember to record your results.

Tensile testing of fabric

Stain Resistance

Stain your fabric with a substance which might be spilt on it during everyday use. Allow it to dry and then try to remove the stain using a method appropriate to the intended use, e.g. tea on upholstery – try removing with a carpet or upholstery cleaner.

Washability

Again stain your fabric samples.

Cut them all to the exact same size so that you can measure them for **shrinkage** after washing. Wash them in a variety of temperatures using the same amount of detergent each time.

Observe and record the following – **stretch**, **shrinkage**, **colour fastness** and **creasing**. Do you think the fabric could withstand frequent washing?

Insulation

Your fabric must be a good insulator if it is to keep you warm.

Fill a glass test-tube with water heated to a set temperature. The test-tube should be fitted with a bung with a hole to insert a thermomether. Retake the temperature after 5-10 minutes and record how much it has dropped. Repeat this test using your fabric wrapped around the tube-test. Also compare the results using different fabrics. Is your fabric the best insulator?

Thermometer
Bung
Test-tube
Heated water
Fabric sample
Rubber band

Stretch and Elasticity

Will your fabric return to its original shape after stretching? Hang strips of fabric, weighted at one end, against graph paper. Make a mark to where the fabric first stretched. Leave for a day and mark again. Remove weights and see if the fabric returns to its original length. You could adapt this experiment to test for **tensile strength**, by using heavier weights.

Drawing pin
Fabric samples
Original length
First mark
Bull dog clips holding coins as weights

OUTWARD BOUND

testing

Abrasion

How hard wearing and durable does your fabric need to be?

Stretch your fabric around a wooden block. Rub with a pumice stone for a given length of time to simulate wear. Which fabric was the most hard wearing?

Absorbency

How much moisture can the fibres of your fabric absorb?

Weigh a range of samples for comparison.

Soak the samples thoroughly and hang them up to dry.

Time how long each one takes to dry.

Waterproofness

How waterproof is your fabric?

Test your fabric by stretching a piece over the top of a jam-jar and spray the top with water. Does any water pass through the fabric into the jar?

Time how long it takes.

Showerproofness

If a fabric is showerproof, water droplets will initially run off the surface, but after a short while start to pass through. Waterproof fabrics will keep moisture out completely. The water will keep running off the surface.

■ **ACTIVITY**

Discuss the difference between absorbency and waterproofness.

▷ If a fabric is not waterproof is it necessarily absorbent?
▷ Does using waterproof material make a garment waterproof?
▷ What else must you think about when designing such a garment?
▷ What sort of test could be devised for these properties?

Crease Resistance

Crumple your piece of fabric in your hand. Does it crease or does it spring back? Devise a five point scale to compare different fabrics.

Flammability

Burning fabrics needs to be carried out under strict safety conditions. Burn only a small piece of your fabric and use tongs to hold it. Observe and record the following

▷ Is there a flame or does it melt?
▷ Is there smoke or fumes?
▷ Is there a strong smell?
▷ How quickly does it catch on fire and burn?

Refer to page 64 if you need to identify the fibres in the fabric.

IN YOUR PROJECT

► It may not be possible for you to obtain a fabric with all the right properties to make your product but you can use a similar one of the right weight for your prototype container.
► Record the results of your tests in a table, and draw conclusions.
► Discuss the difference between absorbancy and waterproofness. If a fabric is not waterproof is it necessarily absorbent? Does using a waterproof fabric make a garment waterproof?

KEY POINTS

● Different fabrics have different properties and characteristics which make them suitable for different end uses.
● Special finishes can be added to fabrics to give them extra properties.
● Various tests can be carried out on fabrics to find out whether they will be fit for their intended purpose.
● Both fibre content and method of construction affect the final properties of the fabric.

Making, Testing and Evaluating Models

Making a model *or mock-up of your idea will enable you to see what your final design will look like, and how well it will work.*

Whether you are making a container or a garment you will need to make up a paper pattern.

After developing your design in two dimensions as much as you can you will need to make a model in three dimensions. This has several advantages:

▷ It will give you a much better idea of how your design would look if made from fabric.
▷ It tests whether the design will work by revealing any faults/mistakes at an early stage. This prevents wastage.
▷ Discovering mistakes before a design goes into production saves time and money.
▷ Cheap materials can be used for a model and a very large design can be made on a smaller scale.

You will need paper, scissors, rulers, pens and pencils, sticky tape, and newspaper, scrap paper or card.

The Container

Put the items which your container is designed for inside your model and see if they fit.

▷ Is the shape of your design the right shape for the items? Are the proportions right?
▷ Try the model on someone and assess whether it will be a good design ergonomically.
▷ Do all the pieces fit together properly?
▷ Are the methods of fastening used strong and sturdy enough?

Is there an easier way to construct your design? Make a careful note of all necessary alterations.

Ask others what they think and find out whether it is likely to attract many customers.

Make sure you record your **evaluation** in your design folder.

1 Estimate the intended measurements and work out the number of pieces required for your container. Draw a diagram with measurements in rough of each piece.

2 You could try your design out in miniature if your design is on the large side.

3 Measure the pieces out in newspaper and cut out.

4 Now stick your model together. Remember that the order of production is important. Pockets need to be made and attached first.

5 Make a note in your folder of how you make your model. Fastenings can be marked on using felt pens.

Experiment with different types of pockets, flaps, fastenings and shapes. How can they best be made interchangeable?

You could also make up your model using calico. (This is known as 'toile')

The Garment

If you are making a garment, sketch the pattern pieces you will need in your design folder. Work out the correct measurements. You may wish to use a commercial pattern or alter a block pattern (see pages 40-41).

Are there any pieces in your pattern which are exactly the same size, e.g.sleeves? If so you will need to make one paper piece and write on it how many times it will need to be cut.

Draw your **pattern** out using the correct measurements on pattern paper and cut out using paper scissors.

All Stitched Up!

Further knowledge of construction techniques will be needed for you to make your container or garment. You will need to practise finishing edges and adding drawstrings, pockets, etc. If possible use samples of the real material.

Detail from cotton seersucker mini dress by Mary Quant, 1972

Material

First of all try **sewing** with the material you intend to use for your container. Sewing fabrics such as waterproof nylon can be quite different from sewing calico. Sew two pieces together using a straight stitch and a plain seam. Experiment until you find the following:

▷ the correct stitch length
▷ the correct needle and thread
▷ the correct tension.

Will you have to tack the fabric together to hold it or will pins be sufficient? Maybe the fabric will stay in position without either.

Finishing Edges

Seam allowances inside the container will need to be finished. Finish both seam allowances together rather than ironing them apart. Try some of the methods on the right. Which will be most appropriate for your construction?

In industry **overlockers** are widely used to finish off edges. They are also used to construct knitwear as they produce a stitch which stretches along with the knitted fabric – an ordinary plain seam cracks when it is stretched.

Another alternative is to simply glue back seams rather than stitching them.

■ **ACTIVITY**

Look inside some of your own clothes and examine how they have been finished off

Overlocking
Overlocking is when a seam is stitched and the edges finished in one operation.

Zig-zag
This can be done on an ordinary sewing machine if you do not have an overlocker.

Top-stitching/edge-stitching
This is used on many garments to give a professional finish and add strength. Sometimes it is done in a contrasting colour. It is always found on jeans.

Adding Drawstrings

Make holes for strings first.

Turn down hem twice – once to finish off raw edge and again to make a big enough casing for the cord to go through.

Put edge-stitching around the top to make it more secure.

Top stitch to give a good finish.

secure cord by knotting the end or alternatively use a cord lock

Making Pockets

Two-dimensional pockets
Find out which methods are available to you. Your school may have an overlocker.

Three-dimensional pockets
These pockets can be constructed from separate pieces.

1 Hem the edges which will not be attached to the bag.

2 Add fastenings if necessary.

3 Press in last three edges and stitch to bag. Position and stitch on flap.

4 Pull flap down and topstitch across the top to make it secure.

Can you work out how to construct a three-dimensional pocket from one piece of fabric? Try it using paper first.

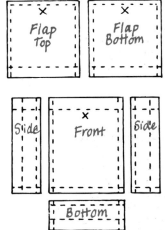

Flap Top

Flap Bottom

Side   Front   Side

Bottom

IN YOUR PROJECT

▶ Mount the test-pieces you have made and label the different types of seams and stitches.

▶ Say which you have chosen to use in your design, and why.

KEY POINTS

● Different fabrics require different stitch lengths, types of needles and threads, and machine tension.
● Overlockers are widely used in industry to stitch and finish seams.
● Pockets can be made in different ways depending on what type/effect is required.

Consumer Legislation

Over the past thirty years laws have been passed to help protect the consumer from manufacturers who sell shoddy or unsafe goods, or who are dishonest in the claims they make for their product. Some of these laws relate specifically to textile products.

Everyone is a consumer of textile products and services. We all buy, hire or rent a wide variety of clothes and furnishings and often need to have them cleaned, repaired or re-furbished.

There are a number of acts intended to help protect the consumer.

The Trades Descriptions Act
This act means that any claims made about the performance qualities of a product (e.g. easy to wash, hard-wearing) must be true.

Consumer Safety Act
This legislation covers of regulations concerning fire and safety hazards, and includes specifications for items such as children's nightdresses, anoraks and fabric toys. For example, the Nightwear (Safety) Regulations of 1985 insist that thermoplastic sewing threads must be used below the waist or elbow in nightdresses made from thermoplastic material.

■ ACTIVITY
GETout have contacted you to ask what legal requirements their new products will have to conform to. What advice can you give them?

Furniture and Furnishings (Fire Safety) Regulations 1988
These requirements clearly state that such products must be resistant to 'smouldering cigarette ignition'. These requirements cover new and second-hand domestic furniture, cushions, pillows and loose furnishing covers.

The Sale of Goods Act
This says that items must be of 'merchantable quality'. If someone is sold an item such as a shirt, then it must perform as one would reasonably expect, e.g. the seams should not come apart after it has only been worn once.

Consumer Protection Agencies
There are a number of organisations that have been set up to help protect the consumer. They include:

▷ Local Authority Trading Standards Offices
▷ Local Authority Consumer Protection Departments
▷ The Office of Fair Trading
▷ The Environmental Health Department
▷ The British Standards Institute.

Planning the Making

Making the model should have given you a good idea of how to go about making your design. Make a list of what you will need. Check that everything you intend to use is available, including tools, equipment and materials.

Tools and equipment

✔ Sewing machine and foot pedal
✔ Overlocker
✔ Fabric scissors
✔ Tailors' chalk
✔ Ruler
✔ Pins

Materials

✔ ½ metre waterproof (red) nylon
✔ Drawstring
✔ Piece of velcro
✔ Red thread

The workspace

✔ Work surface
✔ Stool
✔ Storage
✔ Light source
✔ Electric sockets
✔ Tool, equipment and materials

Organise Yourself

Make sure that your workspace is as safe and convenient as possible by planning how you intend to use it. Using the list of items above, draw a plan of your workspace in your project folder. Label where everything should go so that it is as safe and convenient as possible.

Health and safety is very important both in school and in industry. In groups discuss the safety aspects of working with electrical equipment such as sewing machines and irons and list these in your project folder beside your plan.

Finalise the Making Plan

Look back at the rough plan you noted down when making your model. Make any necessary alterations to it.

▷ At which points do you need to finish off edges?
▷ At which points must you add topstitching?
▷ At which point must you add fastenings. It may not be possible to sew velcro to a pocket after it has been stitched to the main structure of the bag.

Quality Counts

Remember that as your work progresses you will need to check that your work is of an acceptable **quality**. You will need to check

▷ that the width of the seam allowance is even
▷ that your reverses are no longer than 1 cm
▷ that your overlocking is on the edges and has not missed the fabric or cut through the seam.

Overlocking has missed edge

Overlocking has cut into bag

Crooked seam

Untidy reverses

Testing and Evaluating

Your final product must be tested and evaluated in order to find out how well it satisfies GETout's initial design brief and the specification you developed.

As well as testing and evaluating your solution, you also need to comment on how well you have worked.

Testing the Final Solution

Go back to the design specification you wrote for your container or garment. Go through each statement and think about how you can check it. Some things may be very easy to test, while others might require you to set up a special test. For example you might:

▷ test it yourself – for example by putting all the relevant items in it and carrying it

▷ get an intended user to test it

▷ ask an expert such as someone at a local specialist shop or your teacher to try it out and give you their opinion.

If you can, take photographs of your product being used.

Remember to record the results of your tests. Write up the results and conclusions of all data collected.

Criteria	Method of testing	Extent to which it has been achieved
It must carry...	All items put into bag Older brother asked to put items into bag	My container holds all the items intended. A little bit of room for something extra.
Durability	Manager of local trek shop asked for opinion	The main part of the container should last well. The removable outside pocket is rather flimsy.

Evaluating your Designing and Making

In the light of the tests you have carried out, make an overall evaluation of the design you have come up with. You will also need to review the way your design has developed during the project. How successful was the making?

▷ What changes did you make and why?
▷ Did it turn out as intended?
▷ If not, why not?

Use diagrams to explain your answer.

You should also comment on how well you planned your work.

▷ Did you spend too long or not enough time on your investigation, designing, planning, making or evaluating?
▷ How closely were you able to keep to your time plan during the making process?

Improvements

Finish off by making positive suggestions for improvements to the design, and the way you worked.

List the things you could improve if you were to do it again.

Strengths	Areas for improvement
Stitching very neat	I could do more initial ideas as I tend to go straight for the final solution.
Pattern worked really well	
	I could have examined my research material more thoroughly.

Overall quality	Comment
Design – shape	
style	
ergonomics	
aesthetics	
Making – seams	
finishing edges	
techniques	
top-stitching	

OUTWARD BOUND

realisation

75

Examination Questions (2)

If you are following the 'Fashion' option you should spend about an hour and a half attempting the following questions. Before you start you will need to do some preliminary research into:

▷ *special clothing and accessories needed by those taking part in outdoor activities: choose one from hill-walking, sailing or skiing.*

▷ *qualities required in fabrics used for these items.*

▷ *how fabrics can be used for thermal insulation in clothing.*

1. This question is about evaluating features of clothing worn for one outdoor activity. *(Total 8 marks.)* See pages 54-55.

Clothing worn for outdoor activities has a number of special features. With reference to one outdoor activity, give two reasons for each of the following features used on the clothing.

    (i) brightly coloured fabrics;
    (ii) pockets with fastenings;
    (iii) high collars which fit closely to the neck;
    (iv) zip and velcro fastenings.
(8 marks)

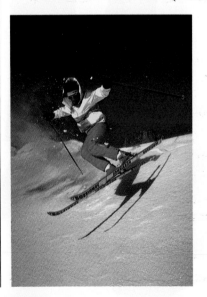

2. This question is about the fabrics used for outdoor activities. *(Total 20 marks.)* See pages 58-61.

(a) Fabrics used for outdoor activities need to have certain qualities.
    (i) Name two qualities needed in these fabrics. *(2 marks)*
    (ii) Describe a test you could do to check whether a fabric had one of the qualities named above.

Give details of:
▷ the equipment you will need
▷ the method to be used
▷ the results you would expect.
(8 marks)

(b) Woven fabrics are used for the outer layer of jackets for outdoor activities. Give two reasons for this.
(2 marks)

(c) A retailer is putting together a booklet of advice for those looking to buy clothing for outdoor activities. You have been asked to write about keeping warm. What advice would you give about using fabrics for thermal insulation of the body?
(8 marks)

3. This question is about the industrial manufacture of garments for outdoor activities. *(Total 21 marks.)* See pages 64-65.

(a) The seams of garments for outdoor activities need special treatment to prevent water from passing to the inside.
    (i) How does the manufacturer of these garments deal with this problem? *(1 mark)*
    (ii) Use notes and diagrams to show how to make a seam that would resist water penetration.
(8 marks)

(b) Give two ways in which computer software can help a manufacturer when planning a layout for garment cutting. *(2 marks)*

(c) Give four costs that a manufacturer would have to take into account when working out a selling price for the garments.
(4 marks)

(d) Discuss whether or not manufacturers should be influenced by current fashion when designing garments for outdoor activities.
(6 marks)

If you are following the 'Furnishing of Spaces' option you should spend about one and a half hours attempting the following questions. Before you start you will need to do some preliminary research into:

▷ *qualities required in fabrics and accessories used in outdoor living spaces e.g. patios, tents.*

▷ *how fabrics can be used for thermal insulation in these situations.*

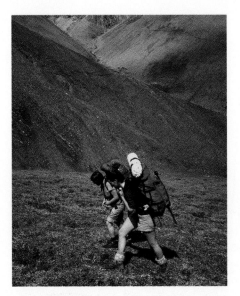

2.   This question is about thermal insulation. *(Total 12 marks.)* See pages 58-61.

(a)   Sleeping bags are often used in outdoor situations. Give a detailed explanation of how these bags keep a person warm in cold conditions.
(6 marks)

(b)   (i) Name two materials commonly used in sleeping bags for insulation.   *(2 marks)*
(ii) For each material named in (i) give two advantages and two disadvantages.   *(4 marks)*

3.   This question is about designing. *(Total 7 marks.)* See pages 34-35, 54-55, 62-63.

(a)   A manufacturer has asked you to design some soft seating for a patio area. Your product will need to be ergonomically sound.
(i) Explain what is meant by the term ergonomics.   *(2 marks)*
(ii) Write a five point specification for the seating.
(5 marks)

1.   This question is about evaluating. *(Total 14 marks.)* See pages 54-55, 58-61.

(a)   Study the illustration of the rucksack shown above.

Label four features which make it suitable for use by people taking part in outdoor activities.

Give one reason why you consider each feature to be important
(8 marks)

(b)   Give three qualities needed in fabrics used for rucksacks for outdoor activities.

Give one reason why you think each quality is important.   *(6 marks)*

4.   This question is about manufacture of soft seating. *(Total 27 marks.)* See pages 38-39, 66-67, 70-71.

(a)   The seating shown below is to be manufactured in quantity and sold nationwide.
(i) Draw a diagram to show the pattern that will be needed. Show the grain line and the seam allowance.   *(5 marks)*
(ii) The diagram below represents a length of 115 cm wide fabric. Show how you would place the pattern pieces to make an economical lay for one seat.
(3 marks)

(b)   (i) How much 140 cm wide fabric would be needed to make one seat?   *(2 marks)*
(ii) How much would be needed to make 100 seats?   *(1 mark)*

(c)   The soft seating will need to be fixed to a wooden chair so that it does not fall off in use.

Use notes and diagrams to show your ideas for two systems for doing this.   *(10 marks)*

(d)   Write an order of work for making up a sample seat.   *(6 marks)*

Project Three: Introduction

*Luxor Travel **need ideas for furnishing fabric designs and a uniform for the crew of their luxury cruise liner.***

You have been asked to design and print a fabric based on an Egyptian motif.

This will be used to help co-ordinate visually the cabins and deck areas and the crew uniform. You will need to make up samples of your designs to present to** Luxor Travel **for consideration.

- Quality Counts (page 122)
- Green Textiles (page 126)
- CAD-CAM (pages 118 and 120)
- Production Process Systems (pages 114 and 116)

The Brief

Luxor Travel would like to commission young designers to create the cabins and uniforms for their luxury ship which will cruise the Nile. They want the designs to reflect the wealth of history, richness of colour and opulence of ancient Egypt.

Furnishings

You are asked to design a fabric suitable for use in the cabin interior. The fabric design could be used for bedding, cushions, curtains, pelmets, etc., or as decorative hangings. You will need to:

▷ design and make a length of fabric
▷ make up one or more of the items above from the fabric you make
▷ produce scale drawings and/or a presentation model of a cabin, indicating the overall colour scheme and where your fabric designs will be used.

Uniforms

Alternatively you could design a fabric and textile logo to be used for a range of uniforms for the cabin crew, e.g. T-shirts, waistcoats, headscarves, etc. You will need to print the fabric and make up one or more of these items.

Manufacturing the fabrics

The fabric and textile products you design would need to be produced in quantity. *Luxor Travel* would need to know how you plan to make the amount they need quickly and to a consistently high standard.

The company is particularly concerned that the fabrics, dyes and construction methods they use will cause the minimum amount of damage to the environment.

They would therefore like you to prepare a short report advising them on how the products will be manufactured in quantity.

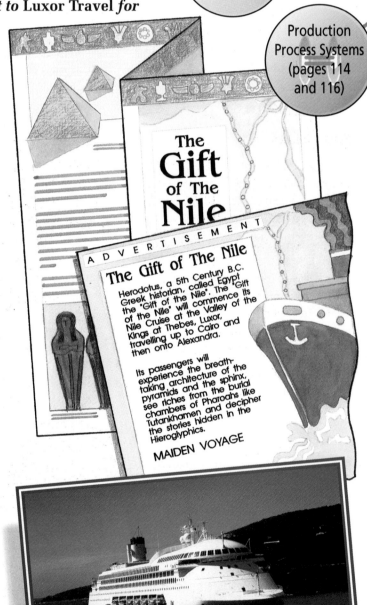

The
Gift
of The
Nile

A D V E R T I S E M E N T

The Gift of The Nile

Herodotus, a 5th Century B.C. Greek historian, called Egypt the 'Gift of the Nile'. The 'Gift of the Nile' will commence its Nile Cruise at the Valley of the Kings at Thebes, Luxor, travelling up to Cairo and then onto Alexandra.

Its passengers will experience the breath-taking architecture of the pyramids and the sphinx, see riches from the burial chambers of Pharaohs like Tutankhamen and decipher the stories hidden in the Hieroglyphics.

MAIDEN VOYAGE

First Ideas

From your research, pick out a range of shapes, colours and patterns that you feel are typical of Ancient Egypt. Begin to manipulate these images by:

▷ changing the sizes of shapes in relation to one another
▷ by repeating a chosen image
▷ by rotating a shape or image
▷ by interchanging the colours
▷ by cutting up a photocopy of a design and rearranging the pieces.

You could use a computer to generate these ideas.

Investigation

Using the library and travel brochures for Egypt from travel agents, research the theme of Ancient Egypt. Find out more about its history, e.g.:

▷ Tutankhamun
▷ Howard Carter
▷ hieroglyphics.

In particular look out for examples of the patterns, textures and colours of the clothes and jewellery worn by rich Egyptian men and women.

What did a typical Egyptian interior look like? Sketch architectural details, patterns and colours. A lot of decorative detail can be found on ceramics and in the hieroglyphics.

Put together swatches of fabrics with different textures, patterns and colour tones which are based on your research. Think about how well they combine together or use complementary colours to provide a more vivid contrast.

Inside Out (1): the Cabin and the Cushion

Colours, textures, patterns and lighting effects all combine together to make interior spaces and places comfortable to be in. The size and shape of the space and how the objects within it, such as soft-furnishings, are arranged, together with the materials used, determine its practicality.

Designing interior spaces

The interior spaces I design are intended to create a comfortable working environment with a distinctive feel. A feature chosen from a particular period in history or from an individual culture can inspire the rest of the space. Colourways, patterns and textures can then be developed through exploring the chosen theme further. Lighting can often be used creatively to enhance the overall effect.

I start by looking at the function of the space and begin to plan around its purpose. For example, a kitchen needs facilities for food storage, preparation, cooking, serving and for washing up. I decide where best to place these areas in relation to each other so that the user can work effectively and safely.

Circulation, or how we move through a space, is very important, especially if there is more than one person in the room.

Next I would look at the most suitable materials for the kitchen furniture, floor and wall coverings, and the soft furnishings. Considerations of scratch,

soil and heat resistance, as well as serviceability for fabrics (washing) are very important.

The shape and size of a room, as well as the amount of natural light it receives, will influence the choice of colours, patterns and textures. A small room, with limited natural light, would favour light colours, smaller patterns, reflective surfaces and the clever use of artificial light to exaggerate the feeling of height and spaciousness. Conversely, in a large, well illuminated space, darker and bolder patterned fabrics could give a more intimate or cosy feel to the room.

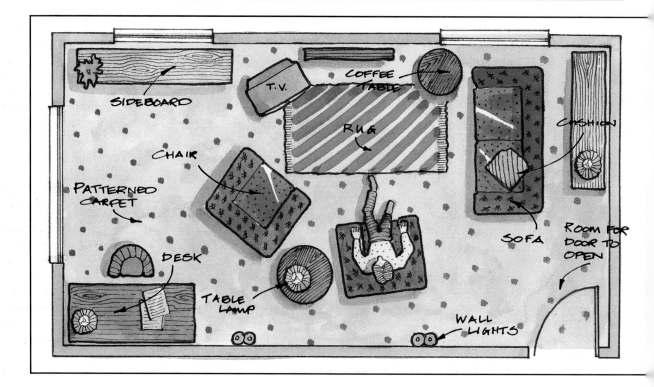

Soft Furnishings

You will need to make a study of how **soft furnishings** are designed, constructed and finished.

Looking at existing products in detail and taking them apart to discover how they have been assembled is a good way to do this. Alternatively, just look at the product and turn it inside out to see how it is constructed.

Decorative design created with coloured fabrics embroidered onto cover

Loose cover

Cotton inner cushion, easy to wash

Stuffing

Care labels concealed inside the loose cover and in seam of inner cushion

Decorative piping and tassel

Hidden zip

Overlocked seam

■ **ACTIVITY**

You will need to find a cushion cover or bolster. Make sketches of the different designs, shapes, fastenings, enhancements and finishes. Describe your findings.

■ **ACTIVITY**

Choose a room at home or school. Describe and comment on the following :

▶ the intended use of the room – does it suit its purpose?
▶ the appropriateness of furniture and fittings.
▶ the circulation through the space – is there room to move easily and safely?
▶ the use of artificial light, e.g. table lamps, uplighters.
▶ the focal point of the room, e.g. TV, fire place, etc.
▶ the use of soft and hard surfaces, e.g. carpet, parquet flooring, patterned and plain fabrics, different textures and mixtures of colour and reflective and matt surfaces.
▶ the use of decorative textiles, e.g. pelmets and cushions.
▶ how noisy the room is without the TV or radio on.

Does the room suit its function? How could it be improved?

■ **ACTIVITY**

Make a study of the work of an interior designer (e.g. Terence Conran). Describe how they use furnishing fabrics to create comfortable yet distinctive environments.

KEY POINTS

● Colour and light can help create a mood in an environment.
● The shape and size of a room influences the choice of colours, patterns and textures used for furnishings.

A SEA CRUISE

products and applications

81

Inside Out (2): Uniform Disassembly

A SEA CRUISE

Uniforms serve many purposes. As well as being practical they say something about the people wearing them, and the company or organisation they belong to.

The shapes, colours, pattern and textures used all deliver messages about the quality and nature of the service being provided.

What effect are the people in the photographs creating by wearing their uniforms?

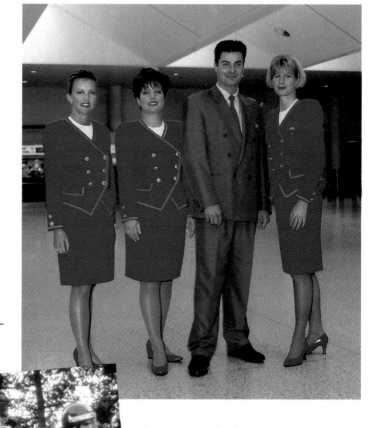

A **uniform** is an easily identifiable set of practical clothes which is unique to the role of the wearer. Uniforms help protect the wearer, ensure a basic standard of appearance, and often indicate seniority.

What we wear is a form of communication, whether we are wearing a uniform or casual clothes of our own choice.

You need to find out as much as possible about the purpose and design of uniforms to be able to define the needs of the company and of the people who will be wearing them.

■ ACTIVITY

1. In groups discuss the different reasons for wearing a uniform.

▷ Are uniforms really necessary?
▷ Do we lose our individuality by wearing a uniform?
▷ Are school uniforms a good idea?

2. Collect pictures from old magazines and make a collage of each of the following:

▷ special outfits worn to show authority.
▷ special uniforms for carrying out particular jobs.

Analyse the material collected. What items does a uniform usually include? What are the specific requirements for outfits worn by people working in the leisure and travel industries?

3. Carry out an investigation into uniforms. Do you know anyone who wears a uniform for work? Devise a survey to find out the advantages and disadvantages of their uniform.

Ergonomics

A uniform must be safe, comfortable and convenient. The individual wearing it must be able to carry out the work required with no restrictions. For example a soldier must be able to move well in his or her uniform.

Ease of maintenance, i.e. cleaning, pressing and repair, is also particulary important.

Garment Disassembly and Evaluation

clean style lines make the uniform look feminine and unfussy

The styling of the jacket is similar to that of a man's suit giving it a strong, smart look e.g double breasted design.

Logo:- smart metal badge

The split at the centre back and the shaped seams aid comfort.

The gold metal buttons and silver trim look expensive and give the jacket definition

Back sleeve seam with opening at cuff which is secured with buttons.

Lining

WAISTBAND cut 2

darts to give shape

FRONT cut 1

BACK cut 1

BACK cut 1

Fabric:
A mixture of wool and viscose. The wool creates warmth and a look of quality. The viscose makes the garment hard-wearing and easy to clean. The fabric is red which makes it easy to identify the Virgin staff and gives them a distinctive image.

■ **ACTIVITY**

Obtain a uniform to study, or work from the photographs above.

▶ Where are the seams, topstitching, openings, etc?
▶ Describe the fibres and fabrics used. How might they have been printed or dyed?
▶ Have any trimmings or fastenings been used?

Try to draw the pattern pieces needed to make each garment.

▶ How has colour been used for these uniforms? Is it effective?
▶ Describe the logos and where they are placed. How distinctive are they?
▶ Is the uniform ergonomically sound?
▶ What do you think of the style of these uniforms?
▶ Do you think they are suitable for the working environment for which they were made?
▶ Can you suggest any improvements to the overall design?

KEY POINTS

● Uniforms convey information about the person wearing them and the company or organisation they belong to.
● They also need to be comfortable and practical.

Ambience and Harmony (1): Interior Spaces

Ambience is the total effect achieved by everything on the ship, including the furnishings and fittings and uniforms. Harmony is achieved when all the different parts adapt well to each other to create a relaxed and comfortable ambience.

By careful planning and designing it is possible to create the appropriate ambience for the intended users.

Ambience

Ambience describes a feeling we get about how well the things which exist in a particular space harmonise together.

When we walk into a room or space it should feel inviting and comfortable to use. One room may be very visually stimulating whereas another may be soothing, but they must both be welcoming.

Different things put together create a good ambience:

- lighting
- colour schemes
- patterns and textures
- hard and soft surfaces to sit on and walk on
- background noise reduced through carpets instead of hard flooring.

Line

Line also has an important part to play in the way we feel. Vertical lines are strong and stable, horizontal lines calming and diagonal lines dynamic. The use of line in your interior design, be it strong architectural features or in the surface pattern of a chosen fabric, can also give off emotional signals to the person using the space. Vertical lines can also make a room seem taller whilst horizontal lines will make it feel shorter and wider.

Lighting

Light in an interior space can create a lot of desirable and dramatic effects, and can be used to highlight features with spot lights or bathe a wall in soft light.

The different colours emitted by electric light bulbs alter the colours of the room illuminated.

Lighting is discussed on pages 24-25 and must be considered if a lot of artificial light is to appear in the interior space. Remember the room will be used in natural daylight as well as artificial light in the evening.

Colour

Can you remember what the following words mean: tint, hue, shade, contrasting, harmonious, primary and secondary colours? Discuss in a small group and write down your answers. The colour wheel and words used to describe the different uses of colour are explained on pages 28-29.

Colour associations

It is important to have an understanding of colour and the psychology or feelings associated with certain colours. For example red, seen in nature as fire, is associated with danger; blue the colour of the sea and sky, is associated with calm; white, the colour of clouds and snow, is associated with purity. What other colours can you think of and what associations do you make with them?

Colours can be described as warm (red and orange), or cool (blue and green), and can strongly influence an overall effect in an interior space. A room interior which is mainly tints and shades of blue would be very soothing, restful and cool. You must consider the effect of colour choices and work towards a desired feel. Try different combinations of colour and describe how you feel when looking at the colour combinations.

Colour plays a vital role in helping the designer achieve the right ambience. Remember that colour can affect our moods. Too much black, grey and neutral colour can make us feel down whereas brighter colours such as yellow may lift our spirits. At the same time too many contrasting bright colours will not help customers to relax.

Colour harmony

Too many colours together can look hectic and unco-ordinated, whereas too few can look co-ordinated but dull. Colour schemes must try to be balanced, harmonious and pleasing.

Choose blends of colour that contrast light and dark tones. The palest colours should be used for large surfaces, the richer colours for decorative detailing.

There are three types of harmony:

▶ Monochrome harmony – tints and shades of the same hues.
▶ Related harmony – made up of small families of hues next to each other on the colour wheel. In order to exercise colour contrast, gradual steps in tone and colour intensity are used to create a visually pleasing effect.
▶ Contrast harmony – made up of contrasting hues opposite each other on the colour wheel.

Colour and proportion

In a room, interior colour can create many tricks of the eye. The cool hues of blues and greens make walls recede, and warm hues of red and yellow make the walls advance. A dark carpet, mid-toned walls and a light ceiling will add the feeling of height to a room. In a room with a dark carpet and ceiling, light walls will look wider and lower.

IN YOUR PROJECT

▶ Experiment with the different light sources on different coloured fabrics and record your findings. Discuss your results in class.
▶ Think about the effect your colour choices will have on your interior space.
▶ It may be useful to get a colour chart from a DIY store and cut and paste your chosen colours together.

KEY POINTS

● Colour schemes need to be balanced, harmonious and pleasing to the eye.
● Colour is important in achieving the right ambience.
● Lines can be used to create optical illusions.

Ambience and Harmony (2): Creating Uniformity

Corporate Identity

All organisations, whether a school or a sea cruise travel company have an identity, although they may not necessarily be aware of it. **Corporate identity** is when the way the company is perceived by the public is deliberately engineered. What a company does and how it does it can all be expressed through the following areas.

Environments

This is the atmosphere created on the boat. This is crucial in putting across the right message to the customer. Visual identity can have the most significant impact so the designer responsible for uniforms, logos and interiors etc. has a vital role to play.

Products and services

This includes the holidays offered by the company and all the services available while on board the ship including entertainment, food served etc.

Communications

This is how you explain what your company does through advertising and any other printed material. Staff are important too as how they communicate with the customer will have an influence on them.

It is essential that all the different elements of a corporate identity system work together in harmony.

Colour and Self-image

We like to wear colours we feel comfortable in and that suit our complexion and colouring. They may also reflect our general outlook on life. For example vivid colours can be worn to reflect an outgoing personality or mood, while paler colours can reflect a quieter personality or mood.

Creating the Right Impression

It is helpful to understand more about the impression the colour of our clothes creates.

▷ Dark blues, blacks and greys suggest respect and authority.
▷ Fawn coloured clothes, especially when combined with soft blue, look professional but are less threatening, so encourage a more open conversation.
▷ Brown clothes suggest a lack of authority.
▷ Green clothes can give an 'off-duty', recreational impression.

Which of these colours of clothes would you wear for presenting your work to a client, interviewing someone or going out for the evening?

■ ACTIVITY

▶ Draw a quick self-portrait. Shade in the colour of your eyes, hair and skin.
▶ Sketch an outfit to harmonise with your colouring.
▶ Sketch another using contrasting colours which would be suitable for going out with friends.

Remember the shape of the garments can create an effect as well.

IN YOUR PROJECT

▶ What sort of image do you think the various staff members should project through their uniforms.
▶ How can colour help achieve this image?

KEY POINTS

● Corporate identity is important in promoting a company and its services.
● It can be expressed through the way in which its environments, products and services and communications work together in harmony.
● The colours people wear create an impression on others.

In the Mood

You will need to do some further research into what people expect and want on a cruise. Creating a mood board will help you find a range of colours, textures and patterns that work well together and appeal to passengers.

Further Investigation

Your research needs to be relevant and can be found in many obvious places: the library, magazines, from talking to experts, etc. **Primary research** involves conducting interviews or experiments to gain new information. **Secondary research** is using information found out by someone else. Your results need to be recorded and presented in an effective way.

Literature search

You will need to collect and collate as much secondary research material as possible in the time allowed. Library books are a good source of text, descriptions and pictures, especially museum catalogues on Egyptian exhibitions (e.g. The British Museum). Brochures from holiday companies provide material that can be cut out. What other sources or research can you think of?

Questionnaire

A questionnaire provides a primary source of information which you can then interpret and apply to your project. You are asked to design a cabin for a luxury cruise liner, so you need to find out what expectations potential customers would have, what facilities they would expect to have in their luxury cabins and what types of finishes to the room they would find pleasing.

Remember to add further questions of your own to the ones shown. Check that the questions will provide helpful information. Present your results in the form of a table.

Mood Boards

A **mood board** is an excellent way of using visual research material. Swatches of fabric and other decorative samples can be presented together. This will illustrate a chosen colourway and how well tints and shades of different colours work together, or in some instances do not work together.

Shapes and sizes

The resources for your mood board should be cut into similar shapes such as geometric (squares, triangles, circles etc.) or organic (asymmetrical or random) shapes of different sizes, or a combination of both.

Don't go for the easy option of just using the shapes your resources come in, but cut them to suit what you want. Think about the size of the base board you will be using. A3 or A2 is a good size, but it could be larger or smaller.

Questionnaire

What age group are you in: 15-25, 26-35, 36-45, 46 and above?

Have you ever been to Egypt?

What images do you associate with Egypt, e.g. pyramids, hieroglyphics etc?

Which colours would you associate with Egypt?

Have you ever been on a cruise?

What would you expect to find in a cabin on a cruise liner?

■ ACTIVITY

Ask your teacher and fellow students to describe what they feel when they look at your mood board. Try to get them to use helpful descriptive words like luxurious, warm, cosy, welcoming, cold, clinical, etc.

▷ Is your mood board successful?

▷ How could you make it better?

You could use your mood board as part of your research to find out what potential customers think.

Use your mood board to get some feedback on your ideas concerning the kinds of fabrics or finishes and colour schemes potential passengers would like to have in their cabins.

Fabric samples

Think about the amount of each fabric that will appear in your interior design or uniform. Try to suggest the same quantity on your mood board.

Very vibrant and rich samples should appear in small amounts if mixed with lighter tones of fabric, otherwise they will overwhelm the desired effect of the final presentation.

KEY POINTS

- Detailed research helps designers decide what will sell well.
- Mood boards can be useful in putting ideas together and promoting images.

Mood

Try to suggest the overall feel of the interior or uniform you want to achieve. Is it organic and free flowing or geometric and ordered? Remember the effect of vertical, horizontal and diagonal lines.

Layout

Before you finally stick your samples down, try several alternative ways of presenting them.

Experiment by mixing different shapes, sizes and contrasts of sheen and matt fabrics, etc. Aim to achieve a good balance of colour and space across the board. Make sure the central area contains the strongest visual focus.

Pattern Repeats

Patterns are developed by repeating one or more shapes and colours. There are a variety of methods which can be used to work out a pattern repeat.

Mirror Repeat

A mirror image reflects a pattern as it might be viewed in a mirror. Fold your paper in half and produce a design on one half of the paper. This image can be turned over and held up to a light-box or window, and then traced.

Straight Repeat

A straight repeat can be produced by repeating your motif at measured intervals, placing each motif directly under the previous one.

Half-drop Repeat

A half-drop repeat is produced by repeating the motif at the side as before, but moving the design half a measurement along underneath, like a brick pattern.

Joined Straight Repeat

A joined straight repeat is produced by:

▷ deciding on the size of your repeat
▷ cutting the paper to size
▷ drawing the motif in the centre of the paper
▷ cutting the sides to join up the pattern
▷ cutting the top and bottom to join up the pattern

Joined up Half-drop

This is achieved by:

▷ deciding on the size of your repeat
▷ cutting the paper to size
▷ drawing the motif in the centre of the paper
▷ dividing the paper to exact quarters
▷ cutting the sides to join up the pattern
▷ joining up the top right quarter with the bottom left quarter to continue to repeat the pattern
▷ joining up the top left quarter with the bottom right quarter to continue to repeat the pattern.

IN YOUR PROJECT

▶ Experiment with the different shapes and colours of your theme to see if you can develop a successful design.
▶ Try out a variety of methods of working out a pattern repeat.

Fabric Blends and Mixtures

Choosing the right fibre and fabric is not always simple. A fibre is rarely perfect and able to give us all the properties we want. Today many fabrics are used which are composed of fibre blends or mixtures.

Blends

This is when two or more different fibres are used to produce a yarn. The fibres are blended before or during spinning. Polyester/cotton is one that is commonly used.

Mixtures

This is when a fabric is made of two or more different fibres, each one spun into a separate yarn. A fabric could have a cotton warp and a woollen weft and it would be described as a wool and cotton mix.

Why have mixtures and blends?

1. To unite the different properties of two or more fibres in order to cover up less desirable characteristics in any of the fibres and give an improved fabric performance.

For example polyester is not very absorbent, dries quickly, does not crease and is easy to iron. Cotton is highly absorbent, takes a long time to dry, creases a lot and is difficult to iron. A blend of both fibres will balance out the properties giving an easy-care fabric whilst retaining the more desirable qualities of cotton such as softness and warmth.

2. To reduce costs by blending or mixing a cheap fibre with a more expensive one.

3. To give different texture and colour effects by using filament and staple yarns which have different textures and dye differently. All fibres do not take up dye easily because some are more absorbent than others. This means that when different fibres are spun together and dyed an interesting effect is produced as the fibres are not all the same colour. This is known as cross-dyeing.

Safety

The ease with which a textile product burns depends on many things including the fibre or blends of fibre used. The chart shows the level of **flammability** of some common fibres.

High Flammability	Low Flammability
Cotton	Cotton treated with flame
Linen	retardants
Acetate	Flame resistant acetate
Rayon	Flame retardent rayon
Acrylic	Polyester
Blends and mixes containing a lot of fibres of low flammability	

Why should polyester cotton be so flammable when polyester is a fibre of low flammability?

Polyester fibres are thermoplastic and normally extinguish themselves by the falling away of the burning molten material. If cotton is present as well it supports the molten polyester and prevents it from dropping and consequently the fabric burns fiercely.

If a cotton sewing thread is used in a polyester fabric the flame will run along the length of the stitching. This is why the Nightdress (Safety) Regulations 1967 insist that thermoplastic sewing threads must be used below the waist or elbow in nightdresses made from a thermoplastic material.

Combining Fabrics

A wide range of the fabrics are now available. Different fabrics can be effectively combined together. The balance between waterproofness, breathability, fabric handling and appearance can be chosen to suit a particular application. For example:

▷ interfacing can be combined with fabric to produce strength and stiffness
▷ quilting different fabrics in layers can provide added warmth.

There are two methods of combining fabrics:

▷ Coating – a layer or layers of a polymer film is applied to the surface of a base fabric.
▷ Laminating – this is when two or more layers of fabric are combined by an intermediate layer of polymer which adheres to both surfaces.

Coated and laminated fabrics are made in many weights and constructions for a variety of applications.

Coated fabrics are frequently chosen for their ability to keep the wearer dry in a storm, while still allowing perspiration from the body to escape. These are often known as 'breathable fabrics'. They conduct the perspiration to the outer surface along a chain of hydrophilic (water attractive) molecules.

Coated fabrics are also used to make protective garments needed in agriculture and industry. PVC coatings applied to cotton or viscose give protection against acid and alkali splashes.

Laminated fabrics allow the attractive appearance of an unstable knitted or lace fabric to be combined with the stability of a woven fabric and provide a much firmer handle.

Gore-Tex waterproof fabric (x100). This resembles a sandwich with nylon outer layers and porous teflon filling

■ ACTIVITY

1. Carry out an investigation into the blends and mixtures most commonly used for clothing and soft furnishings. Use the fibre property chart on page 57 to work out why the particular fibres have been combined. Record your results and conclusions in your fabric swatch book.

In your project folder write down the properties that you think are the most important for the following textile items on board the cruise liner:
▶ uniforms for various crew members
▶ bed linen
▶ soft furnishings.

2. In groups discuss the particular safety factors which would need to be considered for textile products used on board a ship.

3. Carry out an investigation into reversible fabrics. How many examples can you find in everyday use? Record your results in your fabric swatch book.

Uses of laminated and coated fabrics

Leisure-wear:
tents and sleeping bag covers
anoraks
cagoules
overtrainers
gloves
ski-wear
sportswear\footwear

Work:
specialised tarpaulins
survival suits
foul weather clothing
military clothing
surgical clothing
(disposables)
hospital drapes
mattress and seat covers

Rainproof fabric (x30). The outer surface is covered with a polyurethane layer which has tiny pores. This coating is known as 'breathable waterproofing'

KEY POINTS

● Fibres and yarns are often mixed or blended to produce particular properties in a fabric.
● Polyester/cotton is one of the most common blends.
● Some blends and mixtures can result in a fabric that is highly flammable.

Fabric Care

A SEA CRUISE

Because modern textile items are made from a wide range of fibres and fabrics, they need to be laundered in different ways.

Standardising Fabric Care

An **International Textile Care Labelling Code (ITCLC)** which everyone can understand has been developed. This makes it easier to choose the correct cleaning method for each garment.

Manufacturers of washing machines also use this code to standardise their washing programs. The care code appears on labels, detergent packets and washing machines.

In the UK instructions on the use and care of textile products are voluntary, but when a product does carry a label it becomes a legal requirement that the recommendations on the label are appropriate. Such a label should be permanently fixed to the article.

Care Labelling

It is of great benefit to consumers that all garments carry a care label which must state the fibre content of a garment. A good label will contain the following information:

▷ fibre content (this is compulsory)
▷ any special treatments or finishes
▷ cleaning instructions
▷ size of garment.

These labels are permanently stitched into the garment.

Informative Labelling

These labels carry extra information and are only temporarily attached to the garment.

Some good examples of these labels are shown on the right.

A modern industrial laundry

PURE NEW WOOL

The Woolmark was launched internationally by the International Wool Secretariat in 1964. This label may only be used by approved manufacturers whose fabrics have met the quality and performance standards laid down by the IWS. The IWS regularly checks this merchandise to ensure that the textile contains the right fibre content and maintains the appropriate required standard with respect to characteristics such as shrink resistance, tensile strength, colour fastness and moth proofing.

TENCEL®

feel the mystery

Textile Care Code

Washing

Symbol	Meaning
40°	Maximum temperature 40 °C Mechanical action normal Rinsing and spinning normal
40°	Maximum temperature 40 °C Mechanical action reduced Rinse with gradual cooling Spinning reduced
40°	Maximum temperature 40° Mechanical action much reduced Rinsing/spinning normal
(hand)	Hand wash only

Washing continued

Symbol	Meaning
(crossed tub)	Do not wash
CL	Chlorine bleach can be used
(crossed triangle)	Do not bleach

Ironing

Symbol	Meaning
(iron ·)	Cool iron
(iron ··)	Warm iron
(iron ···)	Hot iron
(crossed iron)	Do not iron

Drying

Symbol	Meaning
(circle in square)	Tumble drying beneficial
(crossed square)	Do not tumble dry
(three lines)	Drip dry, soaking wet
(one line)	Dry flat
(arc in square)	Hang to dry

Dry cleaning

Symbol	Meaning
(A)	Dry clean in all solvents
(P)	Dry clean in perchloroethylene
(F)	Dry clean in certain solvents only
(crossed circle)	Do not dry clean

■ ACTIVITIES

1. On the right is a label from a dress.

Explain how the dress should be cleaned.

2. Using the textile care symbols, design a label for a shirt which should be washed at no more than 50 °C on a normal cycle, ironed with a warm iron and which must be hung to be dried.

3. Make your own chart of textile care labels in your fabric swatch book. Use the textile care labels to explain what the instructions mean. Look at soft furnishings as well as garments.

Item	Fibre content	Label symbols	Meaning
Jumper	100% cotton	50°	Maxi temp – 50o
		(P)	Reduced mechanical action
		(crossed triangle)	Do not bleach
		(iron ··)	Warm Iron
		(circle in square)	Tumble Dry

KEY POINTS

- Fabric care has been standardised by the use of a Care Labelling Code.
- Care labels are permanent and informative labels are temporary.
- Fabric care is related to the properties of the fibre(s) and fabric construction.

IN YOUR PROJECT

▶ Brainstorm any special requirements to be taken into consideration when laundering uniforms, bedding (sheets and pillowcases) and soft furnishings.

▶ Investigate whether it would be more expensive to dry clean uniforms or have someone launder them on the premises. What are the implications of being on board a sea cruise liner?

A SEA CRUISE

products and applications

Fabric Printing (1)

A SEA CRUISE

There are three basic methods of printing onto fabric:
▷ **block printing**
▷ **roller printing**
▷ **rotary and flat-bed screen printing.**

The one you choose will depend on the quantity and quality you require and what the fabric will eventually be used for.

You also need to work out the appropriate size and repeat pattern for the fabric.

Block Printing

This craft is over 2000 years old. Traditionally, it is done using wooden or metal blocks. Until 1785, all fabric printing was done by hand blocking. This proved to be an expensive method of producing large quantities of decorated fabrics.

The design is prepared on the block by cutting away the background so that the design area is raised. The dye is applied to the raised surface of the block and the block is then placed onto the fabric. The disadvantages of this process are:

▷ it is very time consuming
▷ it requires a different block for each colour
▷ it is unsatisfactory if fine detail is required.

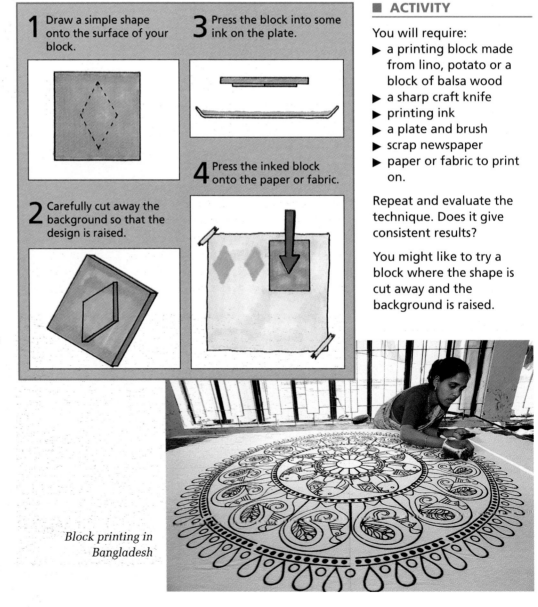

1 Draw a simple shape onto the surface of your block.

2 Carefully cut away the background so that the design is raised.

3 Press the block into some ink on the plate.

4 Press the inked block onto the paper or fabric.

Block printing in Bangladesh

■ **ACTIVITY**

You will require:
▶ a printing block made from lino, potato or a block of balsa wood
▶ a sharp craft knife
▶ printing ink
▶ a plate and brush
▶ scrap newspaper
▶ paper or fabric to print on.

Repeat and evaluate the technique. Does it give consistent results?

You might like to try a block where the shape is cut away and the background is raised.

Roller Printing

Roller printing was invented by a Scotsman called Bell. This method speeded up the production of printed fabrics and allowed the simultaneous application of several different coloured dyes in the process.

The process is cheap to run, but has a number of disadvantages:

▷ the rollers are very expensive
▷ the size of the pattern is limited to the circumference of the roller, usually a maximum of 50 cm
▷ it can be difficult to print large patches of colour without blotches.

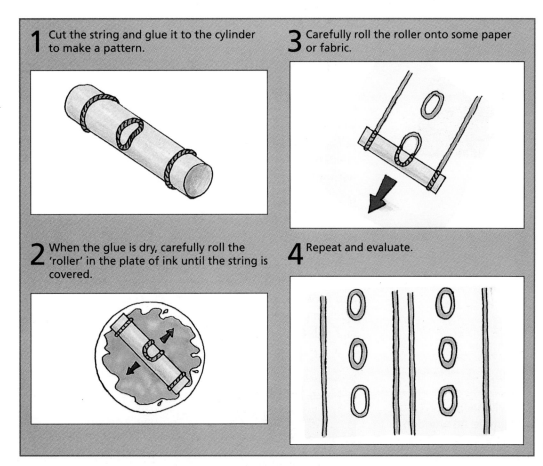

1 Cut the string and glue it to the cylinder to make a pattern.

2 When the glue is dry, carefully roll the 'roller' in the plate of ink until the string is covered.

3 Carefully roll the roller onto some paper or fabric.

4 Repeat and evaluate.

Rotary Screen Printing

Rotary screen printing is the fastest and most widely used process. Modern machines can print over 300 m of fabric per minute. A different colour is pumped into each cylinder and is forced out through a fine mesh screen onto the fabric passing below. The circumference of the roller determines the size of the design repeat.

Roller printing a fabric

KEY POINTS

In industry there are four main printing machine processes:
● roller printing
● rotary screen printing
● flat-bed screen printing
● heat transfer

A SEA CRUISE

enhancement of fabrics

Fabric Printing (2)

A SEA CRUISE

Flat-bed Screen Printing

Screen printing was developed from the stencil printing used a lot in Japan. To stop the middles falling out of stencil designs, little tabs had to be left behind. However in screen printing, the design is placed beneath the fine mesh of the screen, so intricate patterns can be achieved without worrying about the design collapsing.

Screens are economical to print with and complicated designs with fine detail can be printed well. They are also good for printing large areas of colour.

In industrial flat-bed screen printing, the squeegee is replaced by metal rods which are propelled backwards and forwards by magnets below the screen. Many screens can be used in sequence to produce complicated and colourful designs.

■ ACTIVITY

You will need;
- ▶ a simple A4 wooden frame
- ▶ some organdie
- ▶ a stapler
- ▶ masking tape
- ▶ a squeegee
- ▶ printing ink
- ▶ scrap newspaper
- ▶ paper or fabric to print on.

The process of making a screen is covered in Stages 1 and 2. You may not need to do this.

1 Staple the organdie onto the frame as tightly as possible.

2 Stick the masking tape around the underside of the screen where the organdie touches the wooden frame. This will stop the ink leaking out.

3 Make your stencil out of paper, cutting out a simple design.

4 Place the stencil underneath the frame, but on top of a piece of plain paper.

5 Pour a thick line of ink at one end of the screen.

6 Using the squeegee, press down and draw the ink across the screen. Ask someone else to hold the screen to stop it moving.

7 Carefully lift the screen off.

8 Repeat and evaluate.

Industrial Case Study

Andrew Martin International

Andrew Martin International produce fabrics for furniture.

1 The process begins with one of their freelance textile designers developing a fabric which will be suitable to print, and then be fixed and finished.

2 Bleached fabric is used for printing to make sure the colours reproduce correctly. The design is printed through a series of screens. This gradually builds up the pattern, colour by colour.

3 A magnetic roller applies dye evenly over the whole screen, but the dye only passes through the screen where the dye is to appear. This is known as continuous flat bed screen printing. The way the fabric is printed affects the final look.

4 The dyes used are not colourfast, so they must be fixed into the fabric. To achieve this, the fabric is passed through a fixer. This changes its colour however.

5 To restore the original colour, the fabric is given a bath in acetic acid. This acid is then washed out, and the fabric dried again.

6 The cloth is tinted to give it its yellow antique effect. It is then stretched in a drier to restore the original dimensions after its many washes.

7 Finally it is checked for colour consistency, weave and pattern faults before the pattern cutter can get to work. Because the pattern has a strong motif, it's critical that the cutter takes the design into account while he's marking up and cutting.

Specification/Developing Ideas: the Cabin

A SEA CRUISE

You will need to develop a specification and designs for a co-ordinated range of two and three-dimensional textile products for the cabin, based on an Egyptian theme.

You will then need to decide which to print and make up into a sample to show to Luxor Travel.

▶ What different types of floor covering could be used for wet and dry areas?.
▶ Where could you gain extra storage?
▶ Where could you use artificial light sources?
▶ Where could you drape fabric to add interest and drama?
▶ How could you make the cabin look bigger?

Specification

The **design specification** is the set of targets you need to meet. Before you can begin your final design you need a more detailed list of requirements for the facilities, furniture and function for your cabin.

It may be helpful to look at photographs of existing cabins from holiday cruise brochures and makes notes of the list of facilities available. Assume that one to two people will be using each cabin.

▷ How many different areas would the cabin be split into e.g. for sleeping, bathing etc.?
▷ What facilities would passengers expect to find in their cabin?
▷ What furniture would they need?

Specification Checklist

✔ All designs must be based on the theme of Ancient Egypt.
✔ A range of designs for two and three-dimensional products is needed.
✔ The fabrics to be used will need to be...
✔ The fabrics will be printed by...
✔ The length of fabric needed will be...
✔ The number of colours will not be more than...

Spatial Planning

The cabin you will design measures 4 × 4 m square, excluding the bathroom. Using your understanding of scale and plan views, draw an outline and cut out the items of furniture you would expect to find in the cabin. Use these on an outline of the room space to work out where best to place them in relation to each other and to provide comfortable circulation through the space.

It might be helpful to draw the head and shoulders of an 'ergonome', so you can visualise the room in proportion to a scaled down person. Take into consideration access to and from the cabin and bathroom, i.e. opening doors, opening cupboard doors and the locality of the portholes.

Try various alternative room layouts and sketch your ideas, evaluating why you think one looks better than another.

Developing Ideas

From your original ideas you need to become more selective. Choose sample shapes and colours which you find interesting and you think will answer the brief.

You will need to produce a range of co-ordinated fabric designs for the following:

▷ two-dimensional textiles such as curtains, bed-spreads, carpets, wall-hangings, etc
▷ three-dimensional textile products such as lampshades and other furniture coverings, cushions, decorative wall hangings, etc
▷ wallpapers and borders.

Not all the fabrics need to be patterned. Some might be plain or textured.

Those which are patterned will need to contain a variety of pattern sizes and repeats, depending on what they are to be used for. Some might include a large image, e.g. Tutankhamun's death mask, while others might be based on a selection of hieroglyphics.

For each pattern design you will need to explore different colour variations, sometimes called colourways. Think carefully about which patterns go well with each other.

Remember to evaluate each design as you go, saying what you like and dislike about it.

A more harmonious colour combination

Screen print on a cotton/polyester fabric is easy to clean.

Borders for wallpaper or lamps.

Examples of paint or textile colours

A bed throw decorated with a screen printed border and embroidered detail

Machine embroidery is more suitable than a hand made product for this type of mass production

Towels can be finished with patterned tape or a contrasting trimming

Hieroglyphic wallpaper border

Screen printed hanging

printed and embroidered cushion

woven decorative rug designed using Egyptian symbols and colours.

Finalising Your Ideas

As you develop your ideas further you will need to keep in mind what you know about:

▷ the most appropriate blends and mixes of fabrics
▷ fabric care
▷ the possibilities and limitations of printing.

Choose your most successful designs and refine them by working out the pattern size and repeat and the colourways in more detail and accuracy.

If you haven't already done so you need to decide which of your designs you are going to make up. It could be for either a two-dimensional or a three-dimensional textile product.

Specification/Developing Ideas: Logo and Uniform

Before beginning to design the uniform, focus on the limitations and possibilities of your design. You should have a clear idea of the corporate identity you want to create with your uniforms, and the specific requirements for one of the garments (e.g. a waistcoat).

Designing the Logo

Logos should be simple and have an immediate impact. They often contain the name of the company or its initials.

■ ACTIVITY

Make your own collection of examples of logos, particularly those of clothing manufacturers. Mount them in your project folder and evaluate them.
► What makes them effective?
► What message do they communicate about the company?

Work on the graphic aspects of the logo first – outlines and lettering.

Specification checklist

- ✔ The items of clothing which will make up the uniform will be...
- ✔ The impression/style they need to indicate will be...
- ✔ The range of sizes they will need to come in will be...
- ✔ The waistcoat is for...
- ✔ The print on the front must be...
- ✔ The materials will need to be...
- ✔ The colours will be...
- ✔ It must be comfortable to carry and convenient to use...
- ✔ The safety requirements are...

Working in colour

Next work on colour variations – often referred to as **colourways** in industry.

Designers must balance the colours on a design so that one colour does not 'jump out' and break the continuity or harmony of the design. For example a T-shirt might be manufactured in four different colours. Colours for a screen print may work well with one background colour but may not harmonise with another. Pink and grey chosen for the print on a blue T-shirt may not work on a yellow one and therefore must be changed. It can be quite tricky to solve such problems.

Computer-aided design (CAD)

It may be possible to work on your logo designs with the help of a computer. Your school may have a computer-operated embroidery machine on which you could design and manufacture your logo. If not there may be draw/paint packages available to help you.

Developing Ideas

From your original ideas you need to become more selective. Choose sample styles, shapes and colours which you find interesting and you think will answer the brief.

You will need to produce ideas for a range of co-ordinated fabric designs for the range of garments you have identified for the uniform. Not all the fabrics need to be patterned. Some might be plain or textured.

Those which are patterned will need to contain a variety of pattern sizes and repeats, depending on what they are to be used for. Some might include a large image, e.g. Tutankhamun's death mask, while others might be based on a selection of smaller images, e.g. hieroglyphics.

For each pattern design you will need to explore different colourways. Think carefully about which patterns go well with each other.

Remember to evaluate each design as you go, saying what you like and dislike about it.

cotton/polyester side fastening waistcoat. Embellished with an embroidered scarab symbol

yellow cotton with screen printed design and contrasting

Heavy cotton twill is hard wearing and easy to care for.

Sweatshirt design for sports staff or a relaxed occasions

Short jacket with side fastening, could be worn by Male staff with different shaping and a more 'boxy' shape.

FRONT   BACK

Safari style jacket enforces the theme of exploration and is smart and practical. Can be worn with a skirt or trousers.

Unisex trouser design.

The jacket can be worn with an egyptian patterned scarf.

Patterned fabric designs suitable for shirts and scarves.

Luxor logo

Slim fitting jacket with matching skirt or trousers.

Alternative colours with contrasting piping down the front seam.

Finalising Your Ideas

As you develop your ideas further you will need to keep in mind what you know about:

▷ the most appropriate blends and mixes of fabrics
▷ fabric care
▷ the possibilities and limitations of printing

Choose your most successful designs and refine them by working out the pattern size and repeat and the colourways in more detail and accuracy.

If you haven't already done so you need to decide which of your designs you are going to make up into a finished garment to show to Luxor Travel.

Making it (1): a Cushion

A SEA CRUISE

The next stage is to consider the design of the textile product (e.g. a cushion) you are going to make up as a sample.

You will then need to decide which way of printing your fabric best suits your design idea and to organise the correct equipment and the dyes you will require.

You will need to decide on the size, shape and pattern of your cushion design. Cushions can be any geometric shape including square, round, triangular, hexagonal etc., or organic, taking a more asymmetrical form e.g. a leaf, a squiggle, etc.

Side seam zip fastening

1 Measure the size of the zip fastening and mark its position centrally on the seam. Machine stitch along the seam from each corner to the marked points, then reverse about 1 cm to strengthen the ends.

2 Press the seam open. Place the zip on the wrong side, face down, centrally and tack into place.

3 Turn over to the right side and top stitch about 0.5 cm around the zip using a machine zip foot.

4 Remove tacking and finish off threads. With the zip slightly open, place the two sides of the cushion together, right sides facing, tack and complete as shown opposite.

Making square covers

Square covers are the simplest to make. You must measure the size of your cushion pad, length and width ways, and add a **seam allowance** of 1 cm to each side.

1 Cut out two pieces of fabric this size for the front and back panels of your cushion. Remember to cut from the correct piece of fabric, especially if you want one side plain and the other patterned.

2 Place the right sides together (printed sides), with the edges matching. Pin, tack into place and machine stitch 1 cm from the edge. Remember to leave a central opening along one side for the cushion pad.

3 Finish off the beginning and ending of the machine stitching by reversing the stitch on the machine or by over sewing in the loose thread. Trim the seam allowances, snip across the corners, turn the cover the right way round and press with an iron.

4 Insert cushion pad, turn in the raw edges in line with the seam and stitch the edges together.

Making round covers

Measure the diameter of the pad and add 1 cm seam allowance. It may help to make a paper pattern of the circle. Proceed as for the square cover but when trimming, cut notches into the seam allowance at intervals to allow the seam to lie flat.

Embellishments

You may wish to use additional methods of embellishing fabrics to compliment your dying techniques in order to produce the finished design. Will the cushion be patterned on one or both sides, will it have a seamed, piped or ruffled edge?

Remember to decide which embellishments would be best applied before and after the construction of your cushion cover.

Decorative Edging

Ruffled edge

1 Decide on the width of the ruffle (usually 4 to 7.5 cm) and add 1 cm seam allowance. The length of the ruffle should be twice that of the outside edge measurement of the cushion.

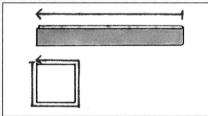

2 Hem the outer edge of the ruffle by turning it over twice at the edge and machine stitching.

3 On the opposite edge run two rows of gathering stitches and gather in the ruffle to the desired length. Tack and stitch it into place. Complete the cushion as on the previous page.

Pleated edge

For a pleated edge repeat as above but pleat the ruffle instead of gathering it.

Planning the Making

You will need to calculate how much fabric you will require. Ensure you print enough to include fabric waste and for any frills, etc., you have included in your cushion design.

Planning the Manufacturing

After you have made up your sample cushion you should think about manufacturing. You will need to prepare proposals for suitable methods of manufacturing the design in sufficient quantity and quality for *Luxor Travel*.

To help you do this, work through the following pages and decide how you could apply the various production and quality control methods to your design.

You may find that you need to suggest modifications to your designs to make them easier to manufacture.

Making it (2): a Waistcoat

Planning the manufacture of your garment will involve producing a pattern, cutting out the fabric and working out the order of making. You will need to draw up a production plan for each stage of manufacture. Include an equipment and materials list and a system for checking the quality of your work.

Pattern Adaption

You may have a **commercial pattern** which you can alter or use the diagram of the **block pattern** below and alter it to create the style of your design.

Test your pattern by making a model in paper or by sewing a sample from scrap fabric. Make any alterations necessary.

Adaptation

The following diagram shows how to alter your waistcoat in various ways.

Planning the Manufacturing

After you have made up your sample waistcoat you will need to prepare your proposals for suitable methods of manufacturing the design in sufficient quantity and quality for *Luxor Travel*.

To help you do this, work through the following pages and decide how you could apply the various production and quality control methods to your design.

You may find that you need to suggest modifications to your designs to make them easier to manufacture.

Designing for Manufacture (1)

A SEA CRUISE

There are many different things that need to be considered when designing something suitable for manufacture. These include its life-expectancy, maintenance, and the need to reduce costs.

What do Textile Designers do?

Designers have to design within considerable constraints.

In the textile industries everything is driven by cost. It is a highly competitive industry both at home and abroad, so to succeed a manufacturer must produce the right goods for the right market at the right price. A designer must be fully aware of all aspects of production, not only the design stage, so that they can consider cost when they are designing.

Materials and labour are the biggest costs. The longer it takes to make an item the more expensive it will be. The same design can be made from differently priced materials. Designers must work with the available materials, components and production processes.

We needed a design which was easier, quicker and cheap to manufacture.

Before
▶ Pleated pockets with flaps
▶ Back and front yokes
▶ Double stitching on collar, cuff, front and back yokes, pockets and pocket flaps, front darts and hem
▶ 100% cotton/denim

Counting the costs

When a manufacturer is faced with a new product a major consideration has to be the way of keeping production costs to a minimum. Some elements will be **fixed costs** while others are known as **variable costs**.

Fixed costs are those incurred in setting up the production line such as machines, the tooling and factory space. Variable costs are likely to be the cost of materials, energy used, the wages of the workforce, insurance and maintenance, etc.

The costs of storage, transportation, packaging and selling all need to be taken into account as well.

The actual cost of the manufacturing of a product in terms of its materials and labour will vary according to the particular item. Often it only represents some 5-10% of the final selling price.

Manufacturers, wholesalers and retailers must make a profit. Many have to move abroad to reduce labour costs.

Design for life expectancy

Customers expect a certain minimum time that a product will last and one that fails before a reasonable time could be very costly for the manufacturer to repair, or in some cases replace.

If the customer's product shows early signs of wear and tear then they are unlikely to make a repeat purchase of the same brand and the brand might develop a reputation for being of poor quality.

However, if the product lasts for many years consumers will not need to buy replacements so often and demand will fall. The number of products that need to be manufactured will therefore drop and as a result the price may well rise. Many products therefore contain components that are likely to fail after a number of years and which would be very expensive to replace. This is called **planned obsolescence**.

Some textile products are designed and made to last longer than others. For example school jumpers and jeans are designed to be hard-wearing whereas an evening dress will not be worn as often and may go out of fashion so it does not need to be as hard-wearing.

After
▶ Simplify pockets
▶ Eliminate yokes
▶ Use single stitching only
▶ Use light-weight denim

Design for Quantity

Products need to be designed to be easy to make. Some items may prove to be very difficult to make in quantity, however. This may be because of

▷ their shape
▷ techniques used on the design: anything very intricate which cannot be done by machine would be very time-consuming to make in quantity and therefore expensive.
▷ the way the components are placed
▷ the cost and availability of the materials required.

Different manufacturing processes and materials may need to be used according to the number being produced. A very expensive dress can be simplified and cheaper processes and materials can be used so it can be produced in quantity.

The rate of production can make a difference too, e.g.:

▷ 10,000 units by the end of next week
▷ 20,000 units over the next twelve months.

Design for maintenance

Designers have to consider how often a new product will need to be maintained during its usage, and take this into account while developing ideas. They will also have to think about how easy it will be to undertake the **maintenance** work. If a component needs cleaning, adjusting or replacing by the user, it must be quick and easy to do. (e.g. buttons are easier to replace than zips or press studs).

For example a uniform that is going to be worn every day must be easily laundered. It must be quick and easy to wash, dry and iron. If it needs dry cleaning it will be less practical.

Ideally a product should be virtually maintenance free, but this is likely to involve the use of higher quality fabrics, components and finer tolerances used in manufacture, which will inevitably increase the cost.

Design failures

Sometimes fashions fail because they are rejected by the public. Designers do not really dictate to the public what they should wear. They must be aware of current and future trends so that they can predict what will be acceptable.

There can be many reasons why a particular design is unsuccessful. Maybe noone wanted it because there was a better or cheaper alternative. Or perhaps it quickly became known that the product didn't wear well. Perhaps not enough money was invested in its promotion, with the result that many people just didn't know it was available, or weren't persuaded that they wanted or needed it. Possibly manufacturing costs proved to be much higher than expected, with the result that the company lost money, and had to cease production.

Finding fault

Much work goes into improving the design of an existing product. Companies often test their products using a variety of techniques to gather information and data so that direct comparisons can be made with other products.

Weaving tests may be carried out as well as fabric tests. Designs may be tested out in certain shapes to monitor the public's reaction to them. Feedback can be obtained through customer services departments within shops.

Sometimes a fault may not be with the original design but in the quality of manufacture.

Self check wool suit by Chanel, 1960

Designing for Manufacture (2)

A SEA CRUISE

The world is a dangerous place. As designers and manufacturers produce new products, they need to ensure that they will be safe to use, and also safe to make.

Safe to Use

The designer must ensure that the product conforms to all the relevant safety standards, including those of other countries in which it might be sold. Careful consideration must be given to ways in which people might misuse the product, and any necessary safety devices and warning labels included: the designer can be held responsible for any accidents which occur as a result of poor design.

There are many laws in existence which help ensure that products are safe to use.

Safe to Make

It is the duty of an employer

'to ensure, as far as is reasonably practicable, the health, safety and welfare at work of all employees.'

(Health and Safety at Work Act, 1974)

There are four main areas to consider in order to help avoid potential accidents:

▷ the design of machinery and tools being used in the manufacturing process
▷ the physical layout of the work area
▷ the training of the workforce
▷ the safety devices and procedures.

In the manufacturing process there are a series of regulations and codes of practice which must be observed.

It is also essential to reduce the number of potential hazards – unsafe acts or conditions – which could occur in the workplace. Accidents are extremely costly in terms of personal distress, compensation and lost production.

Reducing the risks

Although we cannot avoid taking risks, we can take steps to assess the likelihood of something happening, and minimise its impact if it does.

As well as the legal requirements and more general codes of practice for Health and Safety, a considerable amount of documented information is available to help guide the design of safe products and working environments.

Ergonomic studies and anthropometric data can be used to determine optimum positions for displays and controls on products and machines, and the most suitable sizes and arrangements for work spaces and conditions (e.g. the distribution of light, noise, heating and ventilation).

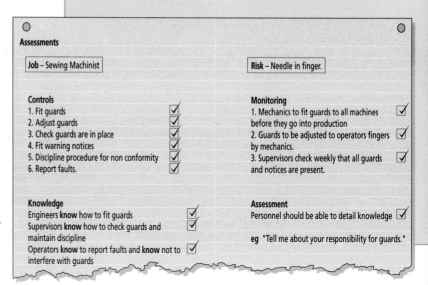

Assessments

| Job – Sewing Machinist | | Risk – Needle in finger. |

Controls
1. Fit guards ☑
2. Adjust guards ☑
3. Check guards are in place ☑
4. Fit warning notices ☑
5. Discipline procedure for non conformity ☑
6. Report faults. ☑

Monitoring
1. Mechanics to fit guards to all machines before they go into production ☑
2. Guards to be adjusted to operators fingers by mechanics. ☑
3. Supervisors check weekly that all guards and notices are present. ☑

Knowledge
Engineers **know** how to fit guards ☑
Supervisors **know** how to check guards and maintain discipline ☑
Operators **know** to report faults and **know** not to interfere with guards ☑

Assessment
Personnel should be able to detail knowledge ☑

eg "Tell me about your responsibility for guards."

Design Issues

When specifying the requirements for a mass-produced product, designers need to consider a wide range of moral, economic, social, cultural and environmental issues. These often produce conflicts which can be hard to resolve.

Moral issues

In certain situations a product may have the capacity to injure or harm someone – either the user or a bystander. Cigarettes and alcohol are obvious examples. Bull bars on cars may look good and help improve sales, but they are likely to increase the severity of injury to a pedestrian in an accident.

Social issues

Some products can have a major impact on the way in which large groups of people live their lives. Convenience foods, for example, mean that there is less likelihood of the family sitting down together to eat a meal. Promotion and packaging can help counter this by providing two-person portions and using images of family meals.

Information and communication technologies are in the process of making a major impact on society, as work and shopping can be increasingly undertaken at home. Advanced automation reduces the number of people needed to produce and distribute goods, causing unemployment.

Cultural issues

The particular beliefs, ways of life and traditions of different groups of people have a major effect on the way they live their lives – what they do, where they go, and the things they buy.

Food and clothing and the symbolism of certain shapes and colours all play highly significant roles in maintaining the identity

of a particular culture. When a product is intended for use by a range of cultures it is important to identify and recognise such needs.

Risk assessment

When a production process involves hazardous situations it is necessary to analyse and assess each particular risk situation and ensure that adequate precautions are taken to minimise the potential danger.

It is the responsibility of an employer to assess the risks involved in each stage of production and justify the level of precautions adopted to a **Health and Safety Inspector**.

Once the risks have been identified they must be controlled and monitored. Below is an example of a **risk assessment** for a sewing machinist.

■ ACTIVITY

1. Design an ideal textiles working area for your school.

List all the tools and equipment needed.

Draw out a plan, positioning everything, taking into consideration safety and ergonomics.

2. Assess the risks involved in each stage of the production of one of the items you have designed and made. List all the employees for whom a risk assessment should be carried out. Use the example shown on the left to say how the risks can be reduced.

3. Carry out an investigation into the different attitudes to dress in your own and other cultures.

IN YOUR PROJECT

Make sure there are statements in your final production design report about:

▶ how much it will cost to make in quantity

▶ how long it might reasonably be expected to last without breaking or wearing out

▶ how frequently and easily different parts will need to be maintained

▶ aspects of the production which might be hazardous

▶ what steps you would recommend to be taken to minimise the risks, and why

▶ how moral, social and cultural issues have been considered.

111

Systems and Control

A SEA CRUISE

To design your product to be suitable for manufacture you need to know about the ways in which industrial production systems are organised.

Systems and Control

A **production system** is an interconnected series of events, materials and components. It is important for a designer to understand something about how such systems work together to make a product.

The role of a **production manager** is to establish how well a system is working and to find ways in which it could be improved, so that a product can be made more efficiently.

System boundaries

All systems are parts of an infinite number of larger and smaller systems. It is therefore essential to begin by defining the particular boundaries of the system to be studied. Supposing you wanted to study a factory production system. Are you going to consider the whole organisation which it is a part of, or just how efficiently one component is being made?

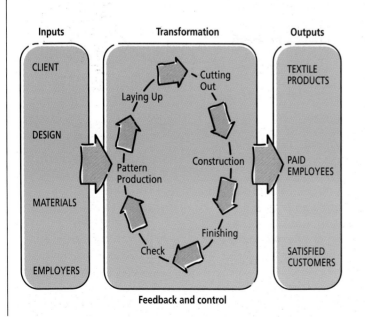

Feedback and control

Inputs, outputs, and transformation processes

All systems have **inputs** and **outputs**. The main purpose of a system is to change or transform the inputs into outputs.

Most systems have many different sorts of inputs and outputs. The first stage in analysing a system is to identify the inputs, outputs and the **transformation processes** involved.

Again if we use a factory as an example of a system, the inputs might include raw materials, employees, manufacturing, equipment, energy, etc. The transformed outputs might include items of furniture, waste materials, paid employees, etc. The factory is a system for bringing such transformations about.

It is also possible to analyse a system in terms of a sequence of events, e.g. collect raw materials, prepare and mark them out, cut them, etc.

Feedback and control

Some transformation processes serve to maintain the equilibrium, or balance, of the system. Others work to improve the quantity and/or quality of the outputs.

It is possible to identify and analyse whether the various processes going on are maintaining the balance or attempting to improve quantity or quality.

When undertaking a **systems analysis** it might be discovered that the quantity or quality of the outputs are unsatisfactory in some way – too much waste material, or products which fail to meet the necessary quality specification and have to be thrown away.

As a result it may be found necessary to change the inputs, or to alter the process of transformation. This is known as **feedback**. The means by which the inputs or processes are changed are called **controls**.

The success of a system is judged by considering how well it transforms its inputs into outputs, and how well it is prevented from failing to work satisfactorily as a result of its feedback and control mechanisms.

In the factory you might be examining the efficiency of a machine which bonds two surfaces together with an adhesive. It might be discovered that the acceptable limits of the amount of glue used are plus or minus 10%. Below this figure the surfaces will not stick adequately, and above the limit the manufacturing costs increase unacceptably.

The question then becomes how to ensure the machine works within these limits?

As well as quality of product or service provision, systems analysis often focuses on achieving acceptable production times.

Analysing a system involves looking at a complicated situation and being able to identify some degree of structure and connection between the things which are going on.

The pockets on our shirts are all crooked. Too much time is being spent on alterations in the pocket section – it is holding up the whole production line.

We collected data and analysed information about the system. We discovered that the stencils used to mark where the pockets should go on the front have not been cut completely straight. When the pockets are marked on using the stencil and chalk they are crooked

By correcting the stencil and ensuring that the chalk marks are in the right position – the machinist can stitch the pockets on straight.

chalk lines

pocket stitched on straght

Undertaking a systems analysis

STAGE 1
Identify and clearly state:

▶ the main inputs and outputs of the system.
▶ which specific inputs and/or outputs you are interested in investigating (i.e. which you suspect to be unsatisfactory in some way)
▶ the parts of the feedback and control operations which need to be investigated (i.e. which you suspect to be un-satisfactory in some way)

STAGE 2
The next step is to collect as much information as possible about the way in which the parts of the system you are interested in works. This may involve collecting factual information (e.g. how long or how often something takes to happen) and opinions (people's observations and comments). In particular you need to try to find out:

▶ what happens when things don't run smoothly, or in an emergency
▶ how the system is maintained over different periods of time.

STAGE 3
Finally, evaluate the extent to which:

▶ the transformation process is over complicated and wasteful
▶ the limits of the feedback system (i.e. the points at which mechanical adjustments or decisions for action are made) are too high or too low

▶ suitable provisions have been made for emergency operation and maintenance
▶ the system can be easily modified to take account of later needs
▶ various changes in the original inputs to the system would improve its performance.

Production Process Systems (1)

A SEA CRUISE

The quicker and easier it is to make something, the more can be made and therefore the cheaper it becomes. This makes the product available to a greater number of people.

What method of production will you be using?

Production Methods

One-off production
One highly skilled craftsperson may produce a single garment over days or weeks. The time taken will depend on the design of the garment and the techniques used to create it. For example a hand-beaded dress will take considerably longer than a simple T-shirt.

One-off production may be used in the theatre where only one costume is required for a specific character.

It is also used by a fashion house wanting to produce a garment to fit an individual customer. This is very costly in terms of labour and materials and only a very small number of people can afford to buy such garments, but these garments are finished to a very high quality.

Art textiles such as wall hangings and creative embroidery are also 'one-offs'.

Batch production
When a specified number of identical items have to be produced a team of people can make them in less time than one person working on their own. The team share tasks and equipment and may become particularly skilled at one or more of the operations involved in the production of the item. Working this way allows for some flexibility so that they can respond quickly to changes in market demand by switching to making a different design. One week they might make a batch of 10,000 T-shirts of one design, and the next switch to making 5,000 units of a completely different design.

Mass production
If a number of workers work on a production line they can each do one part of the manufacturing process before passing the product onto the next person. This enables them to make identical products very quickly eight or more hours a day for weeks or months on end.

Although this significantly reduces time and costs, the whole production quickly halts if there is a problem, and changing the line to make a different product can take a long time.

This method is not necessarily used in clothing manufacture as styles change often. However, some factories may specialise in a few 'classic' products (e.g. jeans, socks, etc) so that the production system can be designed to permanently manufacture them. Using this method it is possible to produce a pair of jeans in 10 minutes.

Fabrics which are needed constantly may be mass-produced, e.g. plain weave cotton. Most production processes involve a mixture of these methods. Some parts might need to be individually or batch produced, while others will be run off continuously.

Different types of manufacturing equipment are needed for the different processes. Some require special purpose tools made to suit a particular product, while others require basic machines with parts which can be changed and re-programmed when needed.

Standardised Design

In many industries a basic **standardised design** is produced to maximise on the economies of large-scale production. Different components, features and accessories, and finishes are then added to the basic design to produce a range to offer the customer

Some styles of clothing stay basically the same, such as shirts and trousers. Only the style details such as pockets, colour and shape may change. This means that a manufacturer can organise production for the manufacture of a basic garment but retain enough flexibility to alter the shape of the pockets, etc.

Standardised Production

Many fabrics (such as plain woven cotton) which are constantly in demand are woven continuously, and then dyed and printed in different patterns and colourways.

In fabric printing silk screens and rollers are used to produce lengths of identical pattern repeats over and over again (see pages 96 to 99).

Pattern lays allow many pieces to be cut at the same time.

pattern

fabric layers

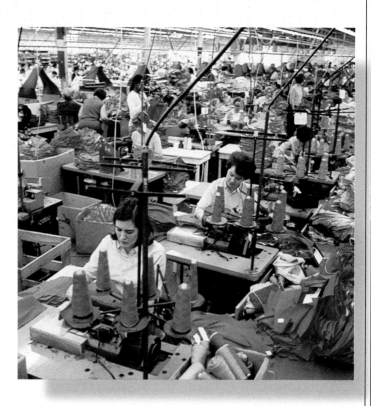

Specialised machinery

As well as using machines which can carry out many different functions, highly specialised machines are used to carry out identical operations which need to be repeated many times. These include automatic dart sewers, buttonholers, hemming units, automatic patch pocket setters, pocket flap-sewing machines, etc.

KEY POINTS

- Most production processes are based on a combination of one-off, batch and mass production.
- Special machines are used to make identical parts or stitches.

Production Process Systems (2)

A SEA CRUISE

It is possible to define the step by step process by which most products are going to be made in simple terms. The different stages of manufacture can then be grouped together into key areas of production.

This flow chart shows the key stages in the production of a waistcoat

When planning a production line, different types of operations are coded by using standard symbols.

Planning a Production Stage in Detail

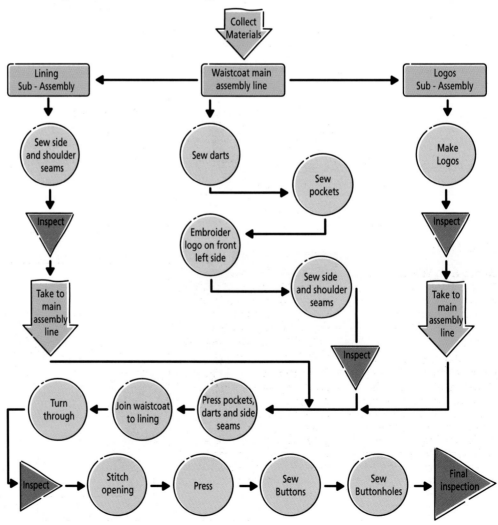

Sub-assemblies

When all the operations have been identified, the next stage is to plan the layout of the **production line**. This is likely to involve a number of **sub-assemblies**, where groups of component parts are assembled before they are added into the main production line. For example the embroidered logo on the waistcoat may be in the form of a badge which has been manufactured elsewhere, bought in by the waistcoat manufacturer and either fused or stitched on.

Sub assemblies are often made in what are called manufacturing cells. These are smaller individual units where four or five people operate specific machines or assemble items. Manufacturing cells are now frequently used in the British clothing industry as the workers can build up a range of skills on different operations. This makes the work-force more flexible, which is important for the production of smaller numbers of high quality garments aimed at a smaller market.

Another way of organising a manufacturing process involves grouping similar machines and/or materials together in one area. This has some advantages, but generally increases the distances that components need to travel.

It is important to ensure that the correct materials and components arrive at the production line at exactly the right time and place. Many factories use a production control system called 'just in time' to ensure this happens in the most efficient way.

A Gannt chart
In all types of production, a complex and accurate production schedule is essential to tell everyone when to prepare, assemble and finish the different components.

CASE STUDY

Birds Eye Walls

Factory layouts and production scheduling can now be efficiently done using computer-based systems.

The Birds Eye Walls CAD system has the power to allow you to fly through three-dimensional views of the factory and see how new layouts will look in practice. Production machines are built up on screen as a series of blocks. These can be moved round quickly to see where they fit best.

Layers (like sheets of tracing paper) are used within the CAD package to hold the details of different services such as water, steam, air and chemicals.

The system is much more accurate than old methods of drawing. Although the initial CAD drawing takes just as long to produce, a great deal of time is saved when changes are made because a completely new drawing is no longer needed each time.

Computer-aided Design (CAD)

A SEA CRUISE

CAD systems make it easy to create a picture of a new design, and then to change the way it looks on the screen. This means that new ideas or variations on an idea can be tried out and evaluated much more quickly than if they had to be redrawn each time.

There are a number of different types of CAD program available. Some are more concerned with the visual appearance of a product, others with technical detail.

Computers have become an integral part of the design, colour and repeat process. They can dramatically cut down on labour and time, and therefore costs.

However designers still need to have an understanding of traditional design aesthetics and hand-painting. The computer is a tool, it will not make design judgements for you.

Computer systems contain three main elements – a series of **inputs** which are **transformed** into **outputs**.

CAD can speed up the entire design, manufacture and retail process. The more new styles you get in the store, the more sales you can generate. Some stores want new styles on the floor every month so they can have maximum newness.

Input	Transformation	Output
A motif or design can be scanned into the computer. It is then ready to be altered.	The computer can make many different repeats and colour combinations very quickly.	Presentation boards giving a good idea of what fabric will look like on a range of garments.

Texture mapping allows a textile design to be draped on a figure in seconds and shows exactly what the final garment will look like draped on a model. Previously the designer would have had to make up the garment to see what it looked like.

Methods of Representation

There are three main ways of representing an object on a computer.

▷ **wire-frame modelling** means that the object is represented by a series of lines. This image can be enhanced by removing lines that would be hidden.

▷ **surface modelling** can be added. The surfaces of the object are represented by colour, shading and texture to give a stronger sense of three-dimensional form.

▷ **solid modelling** where the drawing is based on geometrical shapes which can be mathematically analysed.

Transforming a CAD model

Most CAD programs have certain common facilities. Drawing tools produce lines which can be adjusted for width, shape and colour and can be set to produce curved lines as well. The designer is also able to access a library of existing images which can be added to a design.

It is very easy to transform a CAD drawing or image by copying, rotating and mirroring different parts of it. These functions are usually available on an on-screen menu.

The Impact of IT

Computers are also used to help develop new materials. Special programs can predict the precise physical properties and the performance of new combinations of fibres and finishes.

Du Pont, for example, have recently developed a new bullet and knife-resistant material. Using a computer they were able to predict how far different possible materials would be penetrated and the shape of the indentation. This helped them solve the problem of designing something which achieved the right balance between the effectiveness of the material at absorbing impact and its bulk and weight, which can make it cumbersome and uncomfortable to wear.

IN YOUR PROJECT

Depending on which packages you have at school, CAD could be used to:

▶ create a 3D surface-textured drawing of your idea
▶ produce detailed working drawings
▶ work out the arrangement of pattern pieces that can be obtained from the original fabric.

KEY POINTS

The key advantages of using CAD are:

● it speeds up the process of design development, and as a result a greater variety of designs can be produced.
● an improvement in the quality of design, because the computer can more accurately simulate and produce accurate information about how the design will behave in different operating conditions.
● any changes can be made quickly and communicated throughout the team working on the project.
● design information which has been generated can be stored in a database or file and can be quickly and easily retrieved at a later date.

Computer-aided Manufacture (CAM)

A SEA CRUISE

An increasing number of production processes can now be done by machines which are controlled by computers. Automated manufacturing is safer, quicker, more reliable, and in the long run, cheaper.

Making it by computer

CAM is a term used to describe the process whereby parts of a product are manufactured by equipment that is controlled by a computer.

One of the restrictions of batch-production is that after a relatively small number of products have been made a machine has to be re-set to the requirements of a different product.

The main advantage of CAM is that the new instructions are stored electronically and can be down-loaded and programmed into the machine very quickly. This also facilitates making small changes to the design to suit changes in the market or to produce specialised short-run products for individual clients. Where **computer-aided manufacture** is used to replace a manual operation, greater productivity is possible, because the machine can work continuously. There is also a greater consistency of quality, and fewer faulty goods. CAM systems can also work with materials and chemicals which might be harmful to human operators.

In many cases the manufacture of a complete product is a combination of CAM and hand operations. An example of this may be where the cutting and machining of a panel is completed using the CAM facility but the application of a suitable finish is done by an operator.

Computer numerical control (CNC)

Computer numerically controlled (CNC) machine tools can be independently programmed, but also have the facility to transfer data to other computers. They therefore become part of a complex automated production system. This is particularly effective where a number of smaller manufacturers specialise in the making of a component which contributes to a whole product.

Computer integrated manufacture (CIM)

CAD and CAM systems contribute to the development of computer integrated manufacture (CIM). This is a totally automated production process with every aspect of manufacture controlled by computer.

Powerful CAD systems can be linked into a CIM system. This allows the entire design development, production schedule and manufacturing operation to be undertaken by a single system.

Manufacturing companies which have adopted such systems have been able to make dramatic reductions in the production costs of their products, and increase their quality and reliability.

Making it Somewhere Else

New ways are being developed of creating and sending information electronically.

Computer-generated data about a final design can be sent almost anywhere in the world in a few seconds. The data is then fed directly from the computer into manufacturing equipment to make the product.

Dipdye sarong with silkscreen palm print

Men's palm print shorts, made from cotton with a stencilled motif.

Sundress with built in swimming costume

Fish scale print

Embroidered sarong

Clear plastic bag with printed logos

Rope ties

Cracked wax style batik

Batik, canvas beach bag.

Developing the Final Idea

Develop one idea
in greater depth. In particular think about:

▷ style
▷ material
▷ decorative techniques
▷ finishing and fastenings.

Test Pieces

Make a small sample using the technique and material
that you intend to use.

▷ Is it effective?
▷ Is the technique right for the fabric?
▷ Did it take you a long time?
▷ Do you need to make any
  alterations to your design?

Plan the Making

Identify the different processes
of printing, cutting out,
construction and finishing
you will need to cover.

▷ What tools and
  materials will
  you need?
▷ What needs to be prepared
  in advance?
▷ How will you check the
  quality of making?

Final Testing

Present your final realisation to someone from your
target market.

▷ How did they react?
▷ Did they enjoy trying it on?
▷ Would they wear it?

Final Evaluation

Discuss the process of designing and making you used as
well as the success of your final design.

▷ Refer to the comments made during testing. Do you
  agree with what was said?
▷ If you had more time how would you develop your
  idea further?
▷ How could such a garment be produced in quantity?

Index